Two
Lives

—————————— Peter Marshall. ——————————

Two
Lives

STEIN AND DAY / *Publishers* / New York

First published in Great Britain
by Hutchinson & Co. (Publishers) Limited
First American edition 1963 published
by Stein and Day, Incorporated

Contents

Preface   7
 1 Sitting-up Sleep   11
 2 The Four of Us   16
 3 Three Parts   23
 4 The Ramsey Girl   36
 5 Oakwood   42
 6 The Storm and the Cow   51
 7 Two Days   59
 8 The Interviews   66
 9 "Give Us This Day"   71
10 Illuminations   80
11 Eighteen Years   90
12 In   98
13 Out   103
14 The Ambulance Ride   117
15 The Potato Palace   121

16 The Threads   129
17 Eric   137
18 Home   143
19 Forward and Backward   148
20 The Small Things   161
21 This is the Window   166
22 Humangosophy   168
23 Cards   178

Preface

The word at the head of the penultimate chapter may puzzle: "Humangosophy." It is an ugly hybrid, a clumsy cross-breeding of the words "Humor," "Anger," Philosophy," which are the three bastards of the rapist, "Disability."

In this book I present no Message. These pages tell of two lives, both mine—the first, my eighteen years before the illness, the second, my life afterwards—and of the events and changes of these lives, which are full of everything, except regret.

P. M.

Two
Lives

1

Sitting-up Sleep

"You will sleep sitting up tonight," said the taller Sister, angular as a hatchet.

"Why?" I said.

The tall Sister stiffened into a sword-edge of sour surprise. She was there to command, to be obeyed, not to be questioned by a spaniel-eyed boy with a fat, timid face and a broken arm.

"Because you will persist," she said down her spearing nose, "in rolling onto your arm. That won't do it any good; no good at all. We have to stop that; we have to stop that."

She strutted down the dismal ward, passed the lowered eyes of her patients and the suddenly brisk nurses whose energy was savagely murdered the moment she was gone, down through the green double doors and along the short, brown corridor to her lonely office where she brewed thick tea and kept sentimental love stories, cut from women's magazines, in a locked drawer.

I was alone with the white wilderness of starched sheets and iron pillows and the gray disapproval of tickling blankets. Alone with a broken arm and a torrible problem.

"She must mean on that chair," I thought. The chair beside the bed was small and hard, and it hadn't any arms. "How can I sleep on that? I'll fall over, if I'm asleep I won't be able to stop me. What will she do then?"

I remembered the morning of my arrival, three days and a thousand nights ago: my father, destroying his hat in worried hands, following the silent trolley down the ward to the cream, prison bed; the curious, sizing-up eyes of the other patients; the nurses too busy to smile a welcome; the steel fingers on my elbow, forcing the cracked bone into place; the hateful smell of bandages; the tears fighting the courage of my eyes as my father, head bowed, vanished forever through the green double doors, sacrificing me on the altar of an inhospitable hospital.

I remembered the voice of the next bed, "Wanna comic?"

"Er—no, thank you."

"Suit yourself. What you in for?"

"I broke my arm."

"Same with me, only it's my leg. Came off my bike. Didn't half hurt. How old are you?"

"Six."

"I'm eight and a bit. I'm the oldest, so I'm sort of a boss over the others."

"What's it like? In here."

"Not bad; food's crummy though. Nowt but rice pudding!"

The boy in the next bed raised his head. He had mischievous hair and serious eyes, and he whispered solemnly, "Watch out for Sister, though. She's a witch."

"A witch!"

"Yeah. If you don't behave she takes you into her office and makes you disappear. Forever."

The thin blade of afternoon sun sneered swiftly along the cream-and-green dusty walls. The sun that a week ago had been my own was now betraying me, deserting me to adventure alone around the shining sky like a careless blob of somebody else's blood. I sobbed quietly into my iron pillow.

Suppertime. Mince and left-over-from-dinner rice pudding. The voice of the rice-pudding objector in the next bed calling for more, and the unconcerned clatter of crockery, tightened my fear. I was isolated, a boy who had to sleep sitting on a hard chair. Or else. I pushed my supper away, untouched, and a scowling nurse clucked at me like an offended hen.

Bedtime. A plumping of pillows, a tuck of straying blankets, a slow drowning of light. My last night on earth. I listened to the bed-to-bed, secret, whispered conversations and prayed that the world and Sister had forgotten.

"Sit up, Peter. Come on!"

Sister came up through the floor beside my bed, an evil, sinister, boy-disappearing witch of a woman whose broomstick would be in her office, waiting to fly her home through the lightning-split, thundering night, home to her black house with the crooked chimney and curled-up cat beside the brassy hearth. I sat up.

Sister produced a thing that looked like part of a seaside deck chair and placed it on the bed behind me.

"This is your backrest," she said. "Lean back."

"You mean I—I don't have to get out of bed?"

"Out of bed? Of course not, you silly boy. I can't allow my patients out of bed at this time of night. Lean back."

I did so, and the backrest was as comfortable as patched trousers.

"There," said Sister, "that should stop you rolling on-to your arm. Good night."

"Good night."

She went down the dark and friendly ward, and I sat, as comfortable as a king, in my backrest. I was the only boy in the ward with one. In the morning I would tell the boy in the next bed that Sister was an angel, not a witch. I fell asleep sitting up.

*　　　　　*　　　　　*

My father strode briskly up the glittering ward to take me home. He watched while I dressed, and laughed when I wobbled on my bed-lazy legs. My arm had mended as stiff as a pole. I waved a royal hand to the boy in the next bed and said I hoped that he would soon be able to go home, though I was too full of myself to care very much. I was the wounded warrior returning from a glorious battlefield; my arm, stiff and proud, was a badge of courage and suffering—I would show it to my envious friends and tell them of dark, unknown places where pain was commonplace and ordinary, where boys slept sitting up as though it were the most natural thing in the world.

I was going home with my father, home to my sister Dot, and my brother Ted. Home to my own bed in my own house on my own street. Home to my own life.

2

The Four of Us

We needed that model airplane kit as a dying man needs God, but the combined pocket money of the four of us was one frustrating shilling short of the price. A secret raid on our pantries was planned and executed with the risk-anything courage of desperate men and we rendezvoused behind the shed, out of sight of the kitchen window, and counted the spoils: two cracked beer bottles, one vinegar bottle, three lemonade bottles, one large burdock bottle, four bottles without labels, and a piece of cheese which Jack took because he was hungry. We shared the cheese, and Alf said, "This all we could get?"

"Looks like it," I said. "Dot had one of her clear-outs the other day, there's hardly anything left."

"It'll have to do," said Ted. "Come on."

With bottles in our hands and in our pockets we walked down the hot, gossiping Crescent and the gossip followed us, picked us out, condemned us, "There's them kids from up t'Crescent. Wonder where they got them bottles from?"

"Pinched 'em, shouldn't wonder. You never know what they get up to."

"Somebody wor in our garden last neet. Broke all Charlie's gladioluses. Charlie went out but he didn't see 'oo it was. I bet it wor them little buggers."

"Shouldn't wonder, they're always in other folks' gardens. A good hiding wouldn't do 'em any harm."

"Aye, they're not brought up proper these days. That youngest Marshall's dead cheeky, know what he said to me once . . ."

We turned into the long main street with its smell of diesel and dust and melting tar. The window of the big Co-operative Stores on the corner was whitewashed with impossible boasts: *Lowest Priced Best Bacon. Cheese Down. The Co-op Serves You Better.*

"Go and rub out the t's in *Better*," I said.

"What for?"

"Then it'll say *The Co-op Serves You Beer.*"

"We haven't time to mess about," said Ted. "We've got to get these bottles back. Besides, we might be seen, and we'd have to run for it."

The off-license was old and brown and small, and it

squeezed into itself, afraid of the sun and the heat and the buses thundering past. It was owned by an old, old woman who lived in a shadow at the back of the shop and came out only when you clinked two pennies together. We lined up our bottles on the high, cracked counter, in neat rows like glass soldiers. Our futures as airplane builders were lined up with them. We clinked two pennies, and the old woman shuffled out of her shadow. She kept her empty bottles in a yard at the back of the shop to await collection, and she said, "Been round my back for these?"

"No," we said and noticed how strange the truth tasted.

An eternity in a shadow had made the old woman suspicious of small boys, and she looked at our bottles sat on her counter as if they were boys putting out their tongues at her.

"That's not mine." Out went the vinegar bottle.

"Can't take bottles without labels." Out went eightpence.

The old woman inspected the rest; she twisted them and turned them and sniffed them and searched for the maker's name stamped on the glass. One by one she put them down with a grudging "That one's mine."

She said, "Two beer bottles, fourpence. Three lemonade bottles at twopence each, sixpence. One large burdock bottle, threepence on that. That's—er—one and a penny altogether."

18

We had done it and made a profit of a farthing each as well.

❖   ❖   ❖

For two days we were lost, absorbed in a world of struts, spars, pins, and paper; we covered ourselves and the plan we didn't understand with glue that smelled and tasted of fish; we pinned and glued and papered, then unpinned and unglued and unpapered; we wielded razor blades like drunken barbers; we sang, we boasted, we quarreled.

"This'll be the best plane that ever flew."

"That it will."

"It'll not if you don't watch where you're putting your great foot."

"Mind that wing, idiot!"

"Where's the glue?"

"What daft fool put it there?"

"I did. Watch who you're calling a daft fool."

"Shut up, you two. It's not damaged."

"Anybody'd think I did it on purpose."

"P'raps you did."

" 'Course I didn't. I collected more bottles than you."

"Anybody seen the glue?"

"That bit doesn't go there."

" 'Course it does."

"It's too big."

"I can cut a piece off! What do you think I've got this razor blade for? To shave with?"

"If it wanted a piece chopping off, it would say so on the plan."

"Jack's sat on the glue!"

On the third day it was finished.

We carried it tenderly down the green and gray, glowing Crescent, along the throbbing main street, with its well-remembered, clamoring shops, Mrs. Cooper's bakery, smelling of new bread and teatime on a wet winter's day, and the butcher's, where, if you were lucky, you could see him murdering meat with a giant knife, and blood, warm and living, squirming through his fingers, passed the long, warm wall of the unknown Girls' High School, through our childhood and into the vast freedom of Clifton Park.

"Where shall we fly it from?" asked Alf.

"From Bandstand Hill," said Ted, the eldest, the wisest, and the decision-maker for the four of us.

We ran and laughed through the afternoon park, dodging round elderly working men in their twenties and serious, impossible girls on long legs; three old men smoking their lives away in the hurting sun shook their heads at us; we panted and scrambled up the glaring green thighs of Bandstand Hill, up, up to the towering top where even on the calmest day the wind made the leaves talk.

"Bags first throw!"

"No! Me, me!"

"I'll have first throw," said Ted firmly.

We watched and he held our life in his high hand, waiting to toss it to the drowning wind; for an eternity he tormented us and then he released it, and like a bird it soared and dipped, challenging the sky and mocking the earth and earth-fast people; it sang a silent song of flight and freedom, a miracle created out of useless wood and clumsy paper and hope. I looked at my hands and wondered at their cleverness.

There was a snarl behind us and a brown flash between us. A dog barked down the hill, down to our plane which had landed, small and still and helpless, on the grass. We saw a wing crumple pathetically under a savage paw; we heard the body crunching in pain between cruel teeth. We ran down the hill and saw the tremendous tragedy of our bottle-bought miracle, smashed and crushed and dead.

"Oh, dear me," said a voice. "Has Pom-Pom been a naughty doggie again?"

We turned and saw a woman waddling down the hill, a three-chinned woman in a purple coat like a tent and a feathery, fancy hat.

"Come here, Pom-Pom! Come here at once! Oh, dearie, is that your airplane? Pom-Pom, look what you've done to that nice airplane. You're a naughty doggie, and Mumsie's very very cross with you!"

The dog whined up to her; she picked it up and

lovingly suffocated it in her massive, purple bosom and beamed happily at us.

"Never mind," she trampled on our hearts, "I expect your daddies will buy you a nice new one."

3

Three Parts

The morning was different; it had something special that made it unique among all the mornings of my eleven years. It wasn't special in the way that the first morning of the holidays was special: this wasn't a morning when I could lose myself in childhood, when every stick and gatepost and stone became my allies in adventure and every dark shadow became a hiding place for the creations of my imagination; there would be no dragons on this morning, nor spies to capture, nor grateful girls to rescue from hairy-handed villains. This morning was cold and afraid and important.

And then I remembered: this was the morning I stuck my timid, unwilling nose through the bleak door of adulthood. This was the morning of The Examination.

I remember Ted's advice; advice based on his successful tilt at the eleven-plus. Ted was now at the Grammar School, and I was going to join him there; so I had listened carefully.

"The first part's dead easy, just an intelligence test: 'Underline the odd word in the following—Horse, Cow, Goat, Sheep, Swallow,'—all that rubbish. Any fool can pass that; so you'll be all right. The second part's the worst, it's maths and English You might pass that if the examiner's in a good mood and your English hides the fact that you're hopeless at anything else, maths especially. After that it's a piece of cake. The third part's just an interview at the Grammar School with the bigwigs there. If you do something about your hair and remember your manners you might fool 'em. That is, if you get that far."

Doncaster Road Primary School, Boys' Department, was different. The day-long, chalky prison of the classroom had vanished under a room of new desks, exactly spaced, each with a blotless pink blotter in the center of its unscratched lid. Vanished, too, was the quarreling, sniggering, whispering, boring, roll-on-four-o'clock, scuffling school of every day; this morning each careful desk, each straight pen, each virgin blotter, whispered, "Examination, examination, examination."

*   *   *

For an eternity we waited and wondered and worried. Thirty boys relived the examination night after night; the answer we didn't know, the blot on the paper, the word in the wrong place, the time that ran out, were dark nightmares in thirty sleepless beds; and during the day rumors lived short, fantastic life:

"There aren't any places at the Grammar School, so nobody's going."

"All our papers have been burned."

"Who wants to go to the moldy old Grammar School anyway?"

"Nobody passed, nobody got a question right."

"Spies pinched all our papers, they thought they were atom secrets."

"The Grammar School blew up last night."

"We've got it to do all over again."

"The examiners have gone mad."

"I'm not doing it again. Not likely!"

"Wait till the second part, that's even worse!"

And then, one gray and cold and frightened morning, Old Schofield, our teacher, took a sheet of paper from his desk and said, "I—er—have here the—er—boys who have—er—succeeded in the first part of the —er—eleven-plus—er—examination." He took off his spectacles and polished them on a large white handkerchief. His fingers rubbed slowly round and round each lens as though nothing else in the world mattered, while thirty voices silently screamed, "Get on with it, you old fool!"

He arranged the handkerchief carefully in his pocket,

put his spectacles on his stubby nose, peered over them at us, and said, "The following boys will—er—go forward to the—er—second part of the examination:

Abbot J.

Ackroyd B.

Booth C.

Bryant A. . . ."

Down through the endless alphabet; through the C's and the D's and the E's; there were no F's and the boy behind me, Fingleton K., snuffled noisily. . . .

"Johnson M.

Laurie I.

Mansfield T.

Marshall P.

Martin D. And that's all."

Marshall P. nailed indifference to his face and struggled mightily to keep it there. There was nothing to make a fuss about, he'd never doubted that he would pass.

       *   *   *

The frame was electric blue and the fork-ends were chrome; the handle bars were racing handle bars wrapped with cool blue tape; the slim saddle gleamed blackly; it had a three-speed Simplex gear, and Continental hubs centered the glistening wheels; it crouched, speedy and splendid, in Siddall's window, ignoring my hungry, flattened nose.

It was my bicycle, or would be when I won a place at the Grammar School.

I sat my imagination on the gleaming black saddle and rode it away without anyone knowing. We left Rotherham behind and hurtled in a minute through Doncaster and Thorne; the steepest Yorkshire hill became a tiny slope at a flick of my gears; we whipped through the flat Lincolnshire fields, going faster and faster; my mount was alive under me, and I calmly controlled its steel energy as only I could; on, on to the coast and the sea and beyond, a shining knight on a shining bicycle conquering a kneeling, stagnant world. . . .

I pressed my nose harder against the window as the teatime town flowed past and around, over and below me, drowning me in noise and smoke and sorrow; traffic going nowhere, driven noisily by little people through a dirty, noisy, little town. I was alone with my bicycle and a window, cold as church, was hurting my nose. And then the rumble of traffic began to speak, and it spoke with the voices I heard through my bedroom floor the night after I attempted the awful second part of that awful examination: the voices of my family downstairs, encouraging me with things I shouldn't have heard:

"He must be prepared for disappointment; I hope he doesn't raise his hopes too high."

"You shouldn't have promised him that bike, Dad."

"Give him a chance—he hasn't failed yet."

"I know, but they never pass 'em if they're no good at maths."

"His English is good, for his age."

"That'll not help. He's useless at long division."

"He's useless at addition, subtraction, multiplication, and anything else."

"That's not fair."

"No, but it's true."

"If only he was as good with numbers as he is with words. Clever for his age, that is."

"Mr. Schofield once told him he'd never be up to our Ted's shoulder in maths."

"He's right."

His maths is useless!

His English is good.

His maths is useless!

His maths is *useless!*

His English is——

His maths is useless!

His maths is useless!

The window dissolved into glass numbers, and my bicycle was hidden behind a fence of sneering square-root signs. I walked home, dejected, through the mathematical park.

It was there the next day when I got home from school. It was on the mantelpiece, propped against a fat, brown candlestick, like a bomb waiting to blow a hole in my life. Across its top corner were burned three black words: *Rotherham Education Department.*

Dot said, "There's a letter for you; I think it's about your exam." She dusted a chair that wasn't dusty.

I took the bomb in a trembling hand and opened it; carefully, I drew out my future. I saw: *We are pleased to inform you* . . . and read no more.

"I've passed," I said.

"Never mind," Dot was saying, "everybody can't go to the Grammar—"

"I've passed!" I shouted.

"Get away. Let's look."

I showed her the letter, and she said, "Well, well, so you have. We all knew you could do it if you tried."

    ✵   ✵   ✵

Rotherham Grammar School. A four-hundred-year-old monument to history, devouring schoolboys at one end and ejecting mass-produced young men at the other like a brick worm.

I sat with fourteen other boys in a lonely corridor outside the examination room. From time to time a name would be called by a tall prefect with pimples and a boy would rise, glance round, square his shoulders, and go through the door.

The boy next to me whispered, "Worse than the dentist's, isn't it?"

29

"Yes," I said.

"Think you'll pass?"

"Dunno," I said.

"My dad says to tell 'em I want to be a scientist or a doctor. He says they'll fall for that."

"Yes," I said.

"I don't though. I want to be a Channel swimmer. What do you want to be?"

"Dunno," I said.

"Haven't you any idea at all?"

"Might have," I said.

"My dad says I can have a watch if I pass. Your dad say you could have anything?"

"P'raps," I said.

"Don't talk very much, do you?"

"No," I said.

"You're a bit daft, aren't you?"

"Why don't you shut up?" I said.

The door opened and a boy with a white face came out. The pimply prefect called in a bored, flat voice, "Marshall P."

An endless row of heads, like giant golf balls, were bent over a high, brown table. On my side of the table was a chair, small and hard and lonely.

"Good morning, sirs," I said.

"Good morning. Sit down."

I sat down, and the golf balls ignored me; they were all writing furiously.

"You're Marshall, aren't you?" said the middle golf ball, without looking up.

"Doncaster Road Primary?"

"Yes, sir, yes, sir," I said, answering both questions at once. I hadn't realized it was speaking to me.

The golf ball put down its pen and looked at me. It had a blob of blood on its chin where it had cut itself shaving, and when it spoke the blood performed a little dance.

"Well, now, Marshall," quick-quick-slow, "we have your school record here. Not particularly brilliant at maths, are you?"

"No, sir."

"Why not, Marshall?" cha-cha-cha.

"I think, sir, the subject doesn't seem to interest me, sir."

"And would the subject interest you if you came to the Grammar School?"

"Oh, yes, sir, certainly sir."

"I thought it might. You realize, Marshall, that we expect a boy to have a good knowledge of the basic subjects before he gets here?"

"Yes, sir."

A golf ball at the disappearing end of the giant table shouted, "What do you want to do when you leave school, Marshall?"

What did I want to do when I left school: I wanted to fight in a war; I wanted to be a master spy; I wanted to ride a horse round the world; I wanted to swim the Atlantic with my feet tied together and a bag over my head; I wanted to marry six beautiful women at the same time; I wanted to live alone on a Pacific island forever; I wanted to become Prime Minister and abolish maths; I wanted to win the Pools; I wanted to be a world-champion cyclist.

"I haven't quite made up my mind, sir," I shouted back.

"Have you no idea at all?" said the chief golf ball.

"No, sir."

The chief golf ball whispered to its neighbor, "They're all saying that this morning. Haven't the young any ambition these days?"

" 'Fraid not, Head," whispered the neighbor. "What time is lunch?"

"What are your hobbies, Marshall?" said a golf ball with large spectacles and a little mustache.

"Cycling, sir."

"Very healthy, very healthy indeed. Do you go far afield?"

"No, sir."

"Why not?"

"I haven't got a bike, sir."

"Marshall," said the golf ball wearily, "if I said I was a photographer but didn't have a camera you would think I was pretty silly, wouldn't you?"

"Yes, sir—I mean, no, sir—sir, yes, sir."

"What is your father's occupation, Marshall?" said the chief golf ball.

"Sir, a bricklayer, sir."

"Do you wish to become a bricklayer, Marshall?"

"I don't think so, sir."

"Very well, Marshall; you may go."

"Sir, thank you, sir. Good morning, sir."

They didn't answer; they were bent over the table writing furiously.

I had a dream that night: I was playing golf on a huge, brown, polished golf course. Each time I raised my club the golf ball, which had spectacles and a mustache and a blob of dancing blood on its chin, shouted, "You've no ambition, Marshall, no ambition," and I couldn't hit it.

*   *   *

"The Head would like to see the following boys in his study." Old Schofield called thirteen names, thirteen of the fifteen who had been at the Grammar School. My name was one of them. Two boys were left and they stared, violent and red-faced, at the invisible blackboard, waiting for the earth to open and swallow them, mercifully and endlessly. It is bad enough to fail an examination but to have the failure announced, even indirectly, in public, is worse.

Twenty-six feet clattered up the Headmaster's steep and narrow, friendly stairs; thirteen voices boasted of futures stuffed with glorious, golden promise; thirteen voices boasting and mine was the loudest:

"I'm having a bike, a racing bike."

"I'm having a satchel!"

"Who wants a mouldy old satchel."

"They have hockey and tennis at the Grammar School."

"And Latin."

"It's got a three-speed."

"I'm glad I passed, my dad said he'd belt me if I didn't. He said I was going to the Grammar School or he'd want to know why!"

"Blue it is, with chrome on the forks."

"What is?"

"My bike!"

"Didn't know you'd got one."

We knocked on the door and the Head called, "Come in!" His study was deep and brown and leathery, and he was a deep and brown and leathery man, full of sharp kindnesses and sudden temper. A pair of cycling clips embraced on a ragged blotter; Mr Spearing was a fellow cyclist.

"Aha, boys," he beamed, "I'm sorry I can't ask you all to sit down. I don't suppose thirteen of you can get on the one chair. Ha, ha."

"That's all right, sir," we beamed back, "we don't mind standing."

"I expect you know why you're here."

34

"Yes, sir."

"Yes. Well—er—I'm sorry to have to tell you that you have failed the examination for the Grammar School."

My bicycle shattered, and the pieces were blown to the unknown corners of an unknown world on the winds of a hell of a failure that a million years ago had been a success. Above the rising, piercing wind I heard the sneering, mocking voice of the treacherous Head, "Only two boys from Doncaster Road have passed this year, it seems. I thought it best to break the news in the privacy of my study. That's all, boys; you may go."

We filed down the clattering, bleak, and empty stairs, down into a second-best future. No satchel. No hockey and tennis. No Latin. No Grammar School. No bicycle. No hope. We looked at the floor, the walls, the ceiling, anywhere but at the blank eyes of one another, and the boy with the sadistic father was crying, softly and helplessly.

4

The Ramsey Girl

It grew from a doubtful cloud on the stretched rim of a drowned world into a golden island risen from the shifting sea. The Isle of Man: proud, paddling cliffs and tall, white hotels with many glinting eyes and yellow sand and trees like splashes of green blood. Dots of people crawled along the sweeping Douglas promenade, soaked in sun. The air was like glass, and if I punched it hard enough it would splinter and tinkle into blue space and the world would suffocate.

I could kill the world by raising my fist, but I wouldn't, not yet. I pressed against the warm rail, feeling powerful and generous. The boat was a slow, smoky arrow, aimed at a holiday, stumbling through a crippled sea; I pushed it harder with my impatient chest and my father said, "You'll not get there before the ship, lad."

But the boat was going faster; or was the island

moving while the boat stood still? I was suspended in a bubble of uncertainty, drifting backward toward a carnival. Liverpool, dirty and known, was four hours into the past, and Rotherham was on another world.

❖   ❖   ❖

The fields had just been washed. They rolled and slipped, small and green and yellow, past the window of the bus. The road was a gray smile on a face of freshly washed fields, and the sea curved like a blue beard round its chin.

Ted said, "Look! There's a Manx cat."

"Where?"

"By that hedge!"

But the bus was past, and I didn't see it.

"I bet it wasn't," I said.

"It didn't have a tail anyway."

"Why don't they have tails, then?"

"Don't know."

"Dad, why don't Manx cats have tails?"

"They're born without 'em. Look at the scenery."

The sea trapped the sun in its whiskers, and the fields laughed at the wrestling sun and sea. The sun wrestled free and painted the island with hot gold and cool, black shadow. The bus stopped and burned in a fire of spilled gold on the front at Ramsey.

"Here we are, folks," called the driver. "Back at the bus four o'clock sharp. Have a nice afternoon."

We chattered and clattered out of the bus like thieves fleeing from a camera shop.

Dad and Ted and myself, Drake and Nelson and Henry Morgan, sailed a boat on the stormy Atlantic of a placid park lake and sank all the other boats without wetting anybody.

We drank melting ice cream.

We took photographs of one another sat on the sea wall.

We ate the melting afternoon and photographed it.

We inspected the shops; I bought a book and sat on a green bench fastened to the sea wall while the others went into the park to play crazy golf.

Across the promenade stood a bucket and spade, ice cream, fancy hat, picture-postcard shop, and there was a girl standing in the cool, cluttered doorway.

She saw me looking and smiled.

The sun melted and the sea drowned and in a burning moment of endless time, the world and myself were changed forever. I glued intelligence to my face and studied my book, an intellect with crushing responsibility sitting lightly on my broad shoulders, flipping easily through a work of higher mathematics and advanced science that only a brilliant brain like mine could understand, called *The Avenging Saint*. I held my hand over the title and ignored her with my eyes but not my heart.

She left the shop and walked across the top of my

book; she was slim and straight, and she looked at me with her head lowered and her eyes raised; she sat on the next bench and arranged her flowered skirt around her knees; our eyes met, and she smiled again, shy and friendly.

The melted sun dripped through a hole in the sky and the world shriveled away, except for two benches fastened to a long sea wall in a silent, empty town. I invaded my mind for something to say, some clever and witty remark that would make her swoon with admiration, but my mind was empty like the town. My ears caught the unspoken conversation between a quiet smile and a fat, flushed face on the island of Nowhere:

"My name is Peter."

"My name is Aseta or Zarinda or Mary. My name is Youth."

"Youth?"

"My name is Youth and Sunshine and Laughing-in-the-rain and First-kiss and Broken-heart. We had to meet, sooner or later."

"I've known you a long time."

"Since before you were born."

"How old are you?"

"As old as the first child born on earth and as young as a baby born a moment ago."

"Would you like an ice cream?"

"No, thank you. They make me sick."

"Do you live here?"

"I live everywhere, Peter."

"You're a strange girl."

"No, just a girl."

"Would you like to go for a walk?"

"I've been waiting for you to ask me."

My ears heard but my lips never opened, and the words ran round and round my mind. My book and my past were forgotten, only the future and the girl were alive in a peacock world of sorrow. She got up, my dreams in a flowered skirt and a white, round blouse, and moved away. She stopped and turned and smiled at me; my soul and my heart fled after her, but my body was held to the bench by two great nails driven through my thighs. She walked away, trailing her hand slowly along the sea wall.

"Get up!" I screamed to myself. "She's only a girl! Go and speak to her—don't be paralyzed just because a girl smiled. Get thee hence and conquer!"

She reached the end of the long sea wall. Behind her were fat cliffs and cool caves and soft grass; behind her were dragons, red and fiery, waiting to tremble before my swift sword; behind her was an adventure. She stopped and turned; the breeze moved her skirt, made her sway gently; she was small and lonely and young.

And then she waved to me.

My legs came alive, and I stood up; my heart swelled and pounded in my chest; I put my book into my pocket and started toward the distant end of the sea wall to where she was waiting, waiting. . . .

"Come on!" bawled Ted, from the corner. "It's four o'clock! The bus is going!"

The sun froze and moved on, the sea came back and washed the normal sand; the girl was a white dot I'd never known standing against cliffs I'd never seen. I went to the waiting bus. The driver started the engine, and the bus moved away and I was afraid to look back.

❀   ❀   ❀

Liverpool, dirty and known, was an ink stain on the horizon. A hungry cloud of smoke hung over the crushed and beaten city, full of crushed and beaten people groping for the freedom of their coffins. We began to taste the soot and the grit in the air.

I leaned against the cold rail at the stern of the boat and watched the stretching, widening wake splitting the gray, lost sea. I took a sea shell from my pocket and dropped it into the sea. It vanished, like my holiday, into the empty seas of forgotten time. My father said, "School on Monday, Pete."

It began to rain as we steamed up the stained Mersey.

5

Oakwood

The lion stalked through a dead, trapped jungle in a glass case, and threatened the boy with a stuffed snarl. The boy stood in the black, rusty vault of the museum and snarled back, but the lion didn't blink his fearless glass eye.

The lion would stalk through his mocking jungle into a stitched eternity, unable, for all his sawdust strength, to free himself from his prison of glass; but the boy, thirteen-year-old and mortal, had broken free. Free, with a letter in his pocket to prove it, from a second-best life in a dusty and dull brick, sunless Secondary Modern School at the bottom of a hopeless, cloudy hill.

The letter said: *Dear Marshall, We beg to inform you that you have passed the entrance examination for Oakwood Technical High School, to be opened Sept. 9th 1952....*

The hill wasn't hopeless, the clouds were pierced.

The boy laughed at the prisoned lion and walked from the tomb of forgotten things into the wide, spring park. He was eager for September and his new life at a school that wasn't yet completed. A new school on the same high green hill as the Grammar School at the fresh edge of the town, far from the smoky, treeless gray streets of his Secondary School sentence.

The lion watched him go, envy in his dead, glass eyes.

❀   ❀   ❀

The wind raced over the escarpment and searched the caves of the half-finished school. Groups of boys, shoulders hunched against the knives in the wind, stood on the rough yard. Each group was detached from the others, each clung to a known security. Oakwood was an embryo waiting for birth.

Bricklayers, plumbers, and painters were sculptured about the buildings and yard. Some sat on half-grown walls, some leaned against windows that had no glass, some stared at the wind, and they waited, with the trust of children, for the school to build itself.

The wind whipped snatches of conversation from group to group, like a gossiping woman:

"You'd think they'd have it finished by now."

"They've got eight classrooms done. That's not bad for three years' work."

"Have you heard . . ." whispered the wind.

"Eight rooms! We'll be sitting on one another's heads!"

"I bet you a quid the hall's finished."

"The hall's finished . . ." rumored the wind.

"Can't miss morning service, you know. Got to look after our souls if nothing else."

"Didn't know you had a soul. Wonder where the football field is?"

"No football field . . ." tattled the wind.

"Is that ploughed field our football pitch?"

"Looks like it."

"Look at the slope on it, man. Even you could score kicking down that."

"Want a thump?"

On every morning of importance there comes a moment when the waiting ends and the importance begins. Such a moment came to Oakwood. A man appeared in the doorway of the school and put a whistle to his lips. The groups of boys watched him; the builders stirred and pretended to work; the wind fell silent and waited.

The whistle wailed like a first cry.

It was nine o'clock on the morning of September the ninth, nineteen hundred and fifty-two. The town of Rotherham had given birth to a son, Oakwood.

It was hoped that the infant would survive.

❋   ❋   ❋

44

Everything in the classroom was new. The desks were smooth and bright; the blackboard was innocent of chalk dust; the sticks of chalk in their ledges were long and unbroken; the ink in the inkwells had never known the stab of a cold pen nib. We sat down, slowly and carefully, afraid to spoil the virginity of our chaste classroom. A chair creaked, and the classroom frowned, resented us. A builder peered through the window, grinned, and went away, whistling.

"Wish I was out there," someone whispered.

"Lend me your knife. Must have my initials on this lovely desk."

The door opened, and a brisk man marched tubbily in. He surveyed us for a long moment, then said:

"What are you doing with that knife, boy?"

"Me, sir? Nothing, sir!"

"What is your name?"

"Sir, Marshall, sir."

"Well, Sir Marshall, I'll keep my eye on you. Put that fearsome weapon away and distribute these, one to each boy."

He opened a cupboard door, and I saw shelves of shining textbooks. I reached in and gathered an armful. The title on the gleaming cover of the top book said, simply and painfully: *Mathematics.*

I dropped them all over the brand-new floor.

❊　　　❊　　　❊

"Have you seen the uniform?" said Malcolm.

"I didn't know we were having one," I said.

"You would if you paid attention in assembly. Old Dixon mentioned it some time since."

"Assembly's too early in the morning. Besides, I can't bear to hear your voice raised in noble hymn. Sounds like a blunt saw going through rusty tin. What's this about uniforms?"

The dinnertime yard of the six-month-old Oakwood was noisy and crowded. Among the colored jackets, jerseys, and shirts, one boy, dressed in gray, stood out like a sparrow's feather in a peacock's tail. Malcolm pointed to him.

"He's wearing the new uniform."

"Him! I thought he was a convict."

"No, he's one of ours. Same thing, I suppose. Anyway, that's the uniform. Gray blazer, gray pants, gray shirt."

"Christ! What do they think we are—ghosts?"

"The gray ghosts of Oakwood ride again!" said Malcolm. "And you'll be one of them."

"Like hell I will."

My blazer was gray and the badge on the pocket was an oak leaf and two acorns and the initials O.T.H.S. under them. In it I was superior to the boys still in ordinary jackets. My trousers were gray and so was my shirt, and I wore them with secret pride.

     ❀   ❀   ❀

The football team sang:

"Mary was walking down the glen
Amusing herself with a fountain pen . . ."

and our master in the front of the hired bus pretended
not to hear.

"She dropped the pen and the ink ran wild——"

The back of the master's neck stained red; he swiveled
in his seat and growled, "That will do, boys."

"He must know it," whispered a voice from the
secure depths of the back seat.

The Saturday-morning shops cringed from the singing bus. Women, with dark scarves guarding their hair,
looked at us in wonder, as if singing were unknown to
them; and they condemned us with a sad shake of their
dark scarves. In and out of grim doorways they crawled,
like rabbits in a frozen warren, afraid of song on the
thick, cold November air. They kept their lives in
shopping bags and never took them out.

The shops and the women and the rabbit warren of
Rotherham slid behind us. The pavements narrowed,
became uncertain, then fled back to the town. A new
coldness touched the morning. Fields, gray under the
spewed clay of the outcroppings, lay like worn handker-
chiefs on the earth, and the winding finger of a mine

spun the patient wheels on its tip and sent men into a wound in the side of the world. A tall chimney painted a cloud on the yielding canvas of the sky, and the air tasted of coal.

The bus crept through the desolation like a snail on a shroud.

The driver slid back his window.

"Where's this place?" he said.

"It's the Technical School, just the other side of Dinnington."

The driver eyed his racks, sagging under football boots and cases with mud on them.

"Playing 'em at football, are you?" he asked.

"No," muttered a voice, "we're a delegation from the Anti-Sports League in disguise."

The driver slammed his window, the bus tangled its gears, and our master glared redly at us.

         ✳   ✳   ✳

We kicked and slipped and shouted until our white shirts were patched with mud. Our master paced the touchline, urging us on with dignified shouts of "Play up, Oakwood," and the girls of Dinnington laughed at him behind their hands.

Their center forward, a tall and vicious youth with sharp elbows, received the ball, and I was the nearest defender. I shut my eyes, stuck out my leg, prodded the ball away, and the thirteen-stone hammer of his boot crashed into my ankle. I flopped into a forest of unfriendly legs; mud seeped wetly through my shorts and a fire in my ankle. I wondered where the nearest hospital was and whether or not they would amputate my burning limb. The game surged toward me, and I saw our master performing an agitated dance on the touchline. I thought gratefully that he feared for my safety and was urging the referee to stop the game; perhaps even signaling a passing ambulance. With a groan of relief, I scooped mud out of my ear and listened. He was shouting:

"Get up, Marshall! You're playing them onside!" We lost by six goals to one.

*　　　*　　　*

Oakwood strengthened and flexed itself. New buildings were completed, new departments opened. The cheated wind had to bore new paths round the school. The inside walls held the warm scratches of a thousand scuffles and knew the secrets of two hundred boys. Even in the still night the school wasn't silent: the echoes of one day whispered for the next.

Each morning gray-blazered boys fought and shouted onto the bus in front of the frowning church, and the bus would sway away, groaning and panting.

Other bus queues would forget their childhood and grumble.

"Look at them kids. Don't they know how to behave?"

"Want a good tanning, fighting like that. It's that lot from that new school."

"New school?"

"That one near the Grammar School. Oakwood or something."

"Oh, aye. I know."

The school was recognized, and accepted.

6

The Storm and the Cow

The sun below the horizon shot pink arms along the clear floor of the sky. The waiting air was thin and still. Cattle in the next field, statues of petrified flesh, faced the eastern rim of the morning world, and waited. The leaves in the distant trees were motionless.

The sky was swept with the broom of Dawn: the western edge was dark blue with the dying night, but above our tents the sky was like pale blue paint, and the eastern sky was pink and alive with the waking, flexing arms of the morning.

Our tents were dots on a trembling world, and we stood silently by them, our town eyes hurt by the needles of a country dawn, and waited.

The top of the sun peeped over the horizon, hesitated, then pushed back the blanket of the earth and climbed into the day. The darkness of the western sky fled and a wave of warmth flooded the world with light and life. The cattle in the next field spoke to the warmth; the leaves in the distant trees rustled and danced; a thousand birds shouted at the sun, and Bill put his hand on the electric fence that ran behind the tents.

"Good grief! That's twice I've done that!"

I said, "What were you playing at last night?"

Bill sucked his electrocuted hand. "Me?"

"Yes. You. I woke up to find a flaming dog trotting round the tent."

Ted and Alf, who were sharing the other tent, laughed.

"P'raps he was lonely."

"It's the farmer's Labrador," said Bill. "It was sniffing round half the night so I let it in. Look, it's here again."

A black dog, large as a pony, trotted round the tent and grinned evilly.

"Here, boy."

The dog growled at us, then trotted toward the low, old farmhouse.

"If that brute comes back tonight I'm sleeping outside."

We prepared and ate our breakfast while the sun climbed the hill of the morning and the sky deepened to a hard, hot blue. A stubborn cow voiced a startled protest against early-morning milking, and a tractor spluttered in a far field. The bells of bird voices were magnified by the crystal air, and our traffic-dulled ears throbbed with the sharpness of country sounds.

The sun made a cinder of the morning, and the sounds lost their urgency, then ceased. It hurt the eyes to look anywhere in the steel sky.

"Phew!" said Bill, after dinner. "It's too hot to think."

"That shouldn't bother you."

Ted was stretched face downward, and his voice was muffled with grass: "I'm staying here all day. I'm going to get brown."

"Me an' Pete's riding to Roche Abbey," said Alf. "Coming?"

Bill took off his shirt and stretched whitely on the grass.

"It's too hot for anything," he said. "You'll melt."

      ✤   ✤   ✤

The road was soft under the wheels of my second-hand mongrel of a bicycle, and the air smelled of tar. People sprawled in their gardens, trapped by the sun, and smelled the road and listened with dead ears to the dull traffic. Gardeners shook their heads at their shriveled lawns and panting flowers, then searched the sky for a cloud. But there were no clouds, and the air was gritty and thick with heat.

Strolling summer girls worshiped the sun with bare, pink shoulders and ignored the invitations of our whistles. We jeered at them and wished we knew them.

"I'd like to get that one in a tent."

"What for?"

"Discuss the world situation—what else?"

The houses and the gardens and the summer girls were behind us, lost in the furnace of the day. The sun polished the air, and we rode through pebbles of heat, the clinging road stretching to the end of the hard sky. Our bicycles were heavy and listless.

A voice said, "It's going to rain."

We turned and saw an old, wrinkled face peering brightly at us.

"It's going to rain," repeated the prune of a face, and an old man appeared at a gate in the hedge. "I'd turn back if I were you."

Rain? Rain when there wasn't a cloud in the blue perfection of the sky? Turn back when the afternoon was hot and open and waiting for us? We laughed at the old man and rode away.

"It's going to rain," he cackled after us. "Sure as I'm standing here it'll rain."

We discussed the old man while the road melted and the sky burned.

"He must be crackers! Off his nut!"

"Wonder if there's a looney bin round here?"

"Wouldn't be surprised. He looked as if he escaped from one."

54

"If he goes round saying it'll rain on a day like this they'll sling him in the padded cell."

"I've forgotten what rain looks like."

"It'll not rain today. There's nothing more certain than that."

"Like I said. He's off his nut——"

A drop of rain, large and heavy as a penny, splashed my handle bars. Then another, and another. I gaped upward, open-mouthed. A black carpet of cloud unrolled across the floor of the sky, reached for the sun, and the sun lost its heat and was swept under the carpet like golden dust. The clouds collided, and thunder shocked the ears. Rain shattered on the startled road.

"It's raining," I said, foolishly.

A spear of lightning pierced the afternoon, and the air froze with fear.

"Under that tree! Quick!"

We shivered under the tree and watched through the sudden gloom. The lightning stabbed the afternoon, and funeral drums of thunder played above the saturated corpse.

"Pete," whispered Alf, "what if this tree's struck?"

"Struck?"

"By lightning."

"Well, we can't go out there. Look at it."

Steel rods of rain were hurtling onto the road as though trying to go through it, and they bounced back making the surface of the road the bed of an angry, jumping, restless river. The rain was an animal searching for us, the last people alive on a lost, sodden earth.

"We'll get drowned," I whispered.

We glanced at the mysterious, dripping branches of our tree, then at the curtain of seeking rain, stitched with lightning and heavy with thunder. We were afraid to stay because the tree might bo split with vicious lightning and afraid to leave because the unknown storm would drown us, roll us forever under its surging river of rain....

❧   ❧   ❧

The earth dripped, and the treacherous sun grinned in the damp western sky. The wet, cool earth smelled of shadows and tasted of freshness, and the birds in the distant trees found their voices again. We rode down the puddle-patched farm lane and into the field where our tents were pitched.

"Up here," said a voice.

We looked up and saw Ted and Bill peering through the dark, high doorway of the hayloft.

"What you doing up there?"

"We got flooded out."

"You got—what!"

"Yes. We were in the tent having tea . . . ."

"The plates suddenly started floating . . . ."

"Water came in under the side of the tent . . . ."

"All the blankets and things are wet through ...."

"We must have been in a bit of a hollow ...."

I climbed the ancient ladder and sat in the warm, tickling hay.

"We got under a tree," I said.

"That's a stupid thing to do in a storm," said Bill.

"There was nowhere else to go. Anyway, you weren't all that clever, getting flooded out."

"It was your idea to pitch the tents in the corner."

"Was it hell! It was yours."

"I'll belt you——"

Ted said, "What's wrong with Alf?"

We postponed our argument and looked through the doorway. Alf had been down to the tents, and now he was running back through the wet grass, kicking a spray into the air with his heels. He was waving and shouting and as he came nearer, we heard his words.

"There's a cow in the tent! There's a cow in the tent!"

We gaped at him, then scrambled and fell down the ladder and raced through the grass like speedboats on a stringy sea.

One of the tents was alive, bulging and heaving on the moorings of its guy-ropes. A horn pierced a hole in the tent; the hole became a tear, then a slit running the length of the tent, and the startled face of a cow appeared. She shook herself and the remains of the tent slid coyly round her trampling legs.

57

"Get out of it, you brute!" shouted Bill.

"Too late now," I said. "How did it get in?"

"We must have left the flap open."

"And you said we were stupid for sheltering under a tree."

"We were in a hurry. You'd be in a hurry with water soaking through your pants."

"Why don't you two shut up?" said Ted. "The point is, what do we do now? We can't all get in one tent."

"We'll have to sleep in the hayloft if the farmer'll let us."

"I don't fancy sleeping in no hayloft," said Alf. "There's mice and things up there."

"How do you know? You haven't been up yet."

"There's always mice and things in haylofts."

"Well, we've got no choice. You can sleep in the middle, then the mice'll have to climb over us to get at you."

*　　　　*　　　　*

We slept in the rustling, sweet-smelling hayloft, with Alf curled tightly in the middle. No mice disturbed us, but in the night I felt a cold, curious nose on my face. I opened my eyes and saw the looming shadow of a black Labrador. And Bill's voice whispered in the darkness.

"That bloody dog can climb ladders," he said.

7

Two Days

The corridors of the school were crowded with memories, three years of memories that spoke to me and warmed me. I walked through the slow corridors, and my youth unwound through the passages of time remembered.

This classroom had served as a dining hall at the birth of Oakwood. A stale cabbage stink had fogged this room, this chattering, gobbling, three-years-ago room with the stained tables and narrow benches that needed only a slight, sly pressure from the leg to send them clattering in the middle of Grace. Now the tables and benches were in the great, gleaming dining hall and this room had avenues of desks. Desks and echoes.

And the woodwork shop: a quality of light drifting through sawdust. Even in gray winter this was a golden room. A voice in the empty room spoke to a class that wasn't there.

"Whose are these?" said the voice, and I saw a pair of twisted book ends that should have been straight and I recognized them.

I saw myself raise a hesitant hand at the back of the giggling class.

"You, Marshall. I might have known. How many degrees in a right angle, Marshall?"

"Ninety, sir."

"You astound me, Marshall. Do you think one day you will put your mathematical knowledge to practical use? Construct a right angle from wood or something equally sensational?"

"Yes, sir."

"Take these book ends to pieces and start again, Marshall."

The voice died, the class vanished. The sawdusty room was empty of people. The workbenches were stiff and sorrowful. Only they knew.

Another voice spoke in the deserted corridor, and the English master stepped through the wall of my memory.

"Marshall. A word with you."

"Sir?"

"I've just left the staff room, Marshall. Your name cropped up and I found I was the only master defending your ability as a scholar. You do well in my class, why not in others? Chemistry and maths, for example. I hear your results are very poor there."

"Yes, sir."

"Why, Marshall? If you can do well at one subject why not at others?"

Sir, in chemistry and maths the answers are known; the cleverness lies in finding the correct path to the answer. And there's only one path and that's been trod upon by generations of bored schoolboys. Chemistry and maths are repetition, sir. With English there are no answers and yet there is every answer in the world. When I write, sir, the words are new. Even when they're bad, they're new. With words I can lay my own paths to my own answers.

"I don't know, sir."

"You must buck up your ideas, Marshall. The General Certificate exam isn't far away. One pass wouldn't be very much good to you when you leave school."

"No, sir."

"Remember that, Marshall." The English master disappeared into his lean, brown past, and the corridor was silent. But not for long; my friends were there under the green gloss of memory.

"How many subjects did you get in the General Certificate?" they said.

"One. English language."

"That all? That's not very good."

"That's all they would let me take. One subject, one pass. That's a hundred per cent success."

"Try telling that to an employer."

"Oh, get lost!"

I left the school, and the halls and the rooms and the corridors watched me.

"Where are you going?" said the school.

"I'm leaving. I'm going into the world."

"You'll be small out there," said the school. "Nobody will know you out there. Why don't you stay?"

"I'm sixteen. I've got to leave."

"Please yourself. There's only pain and disillusion out there. Makes no difference to me, though—I'll find somebody else."

"I don't want to leave. I'm sixteen, I've got to."

"There's only pain and disillusion out there!" shouted the school. And I fled down the drive, from the shouting school, from my warm school days, into the worried, working world.

❋   ❋   ❋

I stepped from the bus into the glow of the August morning, and everyone seemed to be watching me.

"See that lad?" they whispered. "This is his first day at work. See that green case he's carrying? Used to carry his football things in that when he was at school a thousand years ago. Now he's got his lunch in it.

Sandwiches. Three jam, three cheese, and an apple. Bet he doesn't eat 'em all. Not on his first day."

I walked past the opening shops, and the haughty, nail-polishing girls whispered behind their counters.

"Look at that lad. Him with the fat face. Starting work today, he is."

"Poor sod!"

"Working in an office somewhere. He was at school a week ago; now he's starting work, and nobody knows him."

"That chap didn't know me last night; didn't stop him trying it on, though. Honestly! The things he said!"

I walked, stiff-legged, through the jungle of wise, magnified eyes, my case bumping heavily against my thigh. I walked through the playground of my sixteen years, and the town was different because this was my first morning at work.

✸   ✸   ✸

"What do you want?" said the red-haired youth.

"I've—er—come to work here."

"Oh, you must be the new chap. Come in, come in."

The office was small and crowded with high, old stools and a huge safe in a corner. Everything was covered with a thin, cobwebby shield of dust, and the air hadn't been changed for a century.

"Through here."

We entered another, smaller, room furnished with a large table and a typewriter. This room was dusty too, and carried a faint smell of stale gas.

"Can you type?" said the red-haired youth.

"No."

"Never mind, you'll soon pick it up. Sit down."

He inserted a torn piece of brown paper into the machine and said, "Practice on this. When you can type I'll show you how to do the invoices."

He left me alone in the dusty, dead room, alone with a torn piece of brown paper and a typewriter I couldn't use. I shut my eyes and stabbed my finger at the keyboard. There was a musical click and a neat, black "p" appeared on the brown paper. I did it again and an "e" joined the "p." Typing was easy.

I covered the paper with black letters that said nothing and made a fence with "m's" and drew a face with the full-stop.

"Very pretty," said the red-haired youth, over my shoulder.

"I'm—er—getting the hang of it."

"So I see. Come with me, my father wants to see you."

"Your father?"

"Yes, my father." He looked down his long nose at me, and his hair seemed redder, as though it were annoyed. "Didn't I tell you?" he said. "My father is the manager here."

*　　　　*　　　　*

I took another invoice from the typewriter, screwed it into a ball, and tossed it onto a pile of other screwed balls of invoices. The hands of the clock pointed to ten minutes to five. The red-haired youth sighed as though something were troubling him and said, "That'll do for today."

"But there's ten minutes to go yet."

"Never mind, never mind. We've got to clear these yet." He indicated the pile of screwed invoices with a tired flip of his hand. We cleared away and put the cover over the typewriter.

"You can go now, Peter. We'll see you"—he shuddered slightly—"in the morning. And, Peter, think about these invoices, they're really quite simple. My father likes efficiency." He addressed that last remark to himself, as though he were beginning to doubt the truth in it.

I walked slowly home through the evening town at the end of my first working day. Nothing had changed; the traffic still ground heavily forward, the air was still thick with petrol. I saw three boys in gray Oakwood blazers; they were laughing carelessly, and I envied them.

8

The Interviews

I said, "I'd like another job."

The youth employment officer tapped his fingers together, and his eyes, behind thick-lensed spectacles, revolved in time with the tapping. The rain drilled into the window behind him, and the bare-board office echoed the dusk.

"I see, I see, I see." He paused for breath. "Why?"

Because I didn't like the dead, dusty, forgotten office that was attached to a living world merely by accident; because the superior manner of the red-haired youth irritated me; because I had typed and posted several hundred invoices and still had no clear idea of their purpose; because that particular morning the manager's son had irritated more than usual; because I had given a week's notice.

"I don't seem to be getting anywhere in my present

job. Besides, I—er—gave a week's notice this morning."

"I see. That was very rash." His eyeballs revolved angrily. "How long have you had the job?"

"A year."

"You're from Oakwood, of course. Let's see"—he took my life out of a large, brown folder—"only the one pass, English. Pity you haven't maths as well. The best jobs go to the boys with the certificates, you know. Five or six passes in the General Certificate of Education can get you any job you wish. . . ."

His voice blended with the drilling rain until both were unheard; the dusk in the office deepened, and the world was reduced to a drilling, ignored voice and two revolving eyes behind glinting glass. It was teatime and I was hungry.

"I said what are you interested in?"

"Oh—meeting people and that sort of thing."

"Mmmm, that doesn't give us much to go on." He pulled another folder toward him, impatiently. "Let's see what vacancies there are." He flipped through the pages. "Clerk in a steel works office; clerk to a corset manufacturer—that wouldn't suit you—office boy in a glass-works office. You don't care for office work, do you?"

" 'Fraid not."

"Factories? Splendid opportunities in a factory."

"I don't care for factories either."

He closed his eyes wearily.

"Farmwork?"

"I don't think I'd be suited to that. All that getting up early——"

"Shops?"

"I've never thought about——"

"Good, good, good." He searched desperately through his folder, his eyes revolving faster and faster. My stomach shrank with hunger. "W. H. Smith need a boy. The booksellers, you know, just across the street there. Your English will come in useful among all those books."

"Yes, well——"

"Yes! Yes! The last boy left because he didn't like working Saturdays. Said he wanted a five-day week like everybody else. You don't object to working Saturdays, do you?"

"I don't think so."

"Good, good, good, good." He fired the words at me like bullets and reached eagerly for his telephone. "I can arrange an interview now."

"You mean—now?"

"Yes. Now." His rotating eyes dared me to refuse. "How about it?"

"Yes, all right." I would never get my tea.

＊　　　＊　　　＊

The shop was closing for the night, slowly, firmly squeezing the last customers through its doors into the cold rain. Inside, the shelves and display stands, tousled by the day, were being tidied by a swift, hurrying girl and another girl was counting coins into neat silver and copper chimneys on the high, cluttered counter. One half of the shop was stocked with books, yellow and red and blue backs of books marching thinly, wisely, to the ceiling and back again, like soldiers but with more importance than soldiers. The other half was a mixture of toys waiting for Christmas and birthdays, and writing pads waiting for letters; the other half was paper clips, pyramids of bottled ink, glass ornaments, useless and beautiful, racks of greeting cards, files, fountain pens, T-squares, drawing boards, slide rules, brief cases, bamboo table mats, toy trains and Teddy bears, and the stately stand of typewriters.

Oh! I liked the smell and the color and the challenge of the shop.

The manager said: "There's no limit to the opportunity at W. H. Smith. Manager, area manager, board of directors even. Provided a boy's prepared to work hard, of course."

No limit. No dust. No invoices of mystery and misery. No red-haired manager's son with superior manner.

"You'll work here in Rotherham for three or four years then travel round other shops to get experience. Then you'll be a relief manager, you know, taking over shops when the regular manager's on holiday or ill. And after that, all being well, a shop of your own."

Travel. A shop of my own. No dead, rusty office chains. We arranged the details of the job; then I left and laughed through the dripping park, and even the rain seemed friendly.

For a week I smirked my triumph at the manager's son and doodled on his invoices and ignored the trapped gloom of his buried office. The world was living outside, and I was going to live with it, forge my own life on my own anvil. And even the remark of the manager's son, on my last afternoon, didn't annoy me. He pointed his red hair at me and sneered, "Frankly, the retail business is welcome to you."

I smiled under a straight, stiff face, and on my way out I kicked him, hard, on the shin.

9

"*Give Us This Day*"

The organ's sad song lapped the prim, Sunday walls of the grim Methodist chapel, and ebbed into the Sunday hearts of the rustling congregation. The hard, narrow pews stood to attention under the Sunday-stiff bottoms of the worshipers, and the high, dark windows made an enemy of the evening and refused it entrance.

The choir filed solemnly into their places, higher than the rest of us, and opened their thick hymn books. The chapel became a clearing of starched throats, a communal dislodging of Sunday phlegm.

The Minister entered on the wings of his flowing robes. A black Bible was in his arms, and God was in his head. He was a bargainer, the Minister: if we sang his empty hymns he would open his head and show us God; if we closed our brains we could see God in his proud, noble head.

The organ whimpered into silence, and the Minister commanded us through the razors of his Sunday lips, "We will sing hymn No. 403. . . ."

The organ coughed, found the right key and the congregation clattered to its feet with a crackle of once-a-week clothes and paid Sunday homage to a tone-deaf God. And the voice which came to my head every Sunday came again with more insistence than usual.

"What are you doing here?" accused the voice inside my head.

"Because, well, just because!"

"You don't really know, do you?" sneered the voice.

I looked at my friends, involved with their hymn books, and I looked along the other pews stuffed with people opening and closing their mouths like fish waiting for the worm of God. And the voice was right: I didn't know.

"I'm here because my friends are here," I muttered. "I have to go somewhere. Why not here?"

"Are you a fish, too?" said the voice. "A chanting, praying block of a fish with an empty head. A fish eager for God's hook in your soft mouth?"

"That mightn't be so bad."

"How do you know? How do you even know there is a God?"

"There's always been a God. Ever since I was born."

"That's not always," said the voice.

"Well, you know what I mean. Anyway, the Minister has God."

"Only in his head. And he can't prove even that."

"You don't need proof. You just have to believe."

The voice laughed inside my head. "Exactly. And you don't really believe. You think there might be a God so you play it safe by coming to this place once a week. All this hymning and praying and preaching, it's above you."

"I——!"

"You stick a regular sixpence in the slot machine, hoping for the jackpot when you shuffle off."

"Shuffle off?"

"Die. You will one day. And you think by coming to chapel you'll get life hereafter. But you don't really believe."

"There might be a God. There might be another life."

"Of course there might," said the voice. "But you have to believe, really believe. If you don't you shouldn't be here. That's dishonest. You're a fish, Peter Marshall, a dishonest, hopeful fish. You shouldn't be here."

The hymn mourned up to the ceiling and stopped. The congregation slapped their bottoms onto the hard pews and were still. The black-robed Minister, with a head full of God, opened his Bible. Max, sitting stiffly next to me, whispered, "You going on this midnight-hike thing next week?"

"Yes."

"Always thought you were a bit mad."

I grinned and strangled the voice in my head with the thin string of security. The Minister took his long words from his bible and flung them at us. He took life from his bible and tossed it to us like an old coat and his God said, "Try it on—it might fit."

And the choking voice in my head whispered, "It'll not fit you, you're the wrong shape," then rattled into death.

"Didn't hear you singing that last hymn," muttered Max.

"I was thinking."

"Thought I could smell wood burning. What about?"

"Oh, nothing very much," I said. "Just this midnight-hike lark."

*   *   *

A crocodile of young people crawled through the Derbyshire darkness. A crocodile warding off the night with thick sweaters and thicker socks. Young people with rucksacks and cases and thermos flasks. A crocodile wading into the night.

The cobbled, hissing, yellow yard of Hope Station was behind us; the Saturday-night cavern of Sheffield was a fading memory, and the card-clamoring, book-browsing worriers of my July working day might never have existed.

The full night stretched into blackness.

Whispers tiptoed carefully, slowly, along the back of the crocodile, afraid to break the night.

"When will we get there?"

" 'Bout midnight."

"Don't fancy climbing that hill in the dark."

"Well, that's where the service is going to be."

"Why on top of a hill?"

"P'raps they want to get nearer Heaven."

"What you brought to eat?"

"Sandwiches. Cheese."

"I've got some soup in a flask."

"I wish I were back home in bed."

"Talking of beds, have you seen that blonde back there?"

"We're going to a religious service—not an orgy."

"I know, but you never know your luck."

"My mum'd kill me if she knew all these boys were here."

"Doesn't she know, then?"

"I told her only girls were going with the Vicar."

"You're safe enough."

"You don't know what might happen in the dark."

"I've got a blanket in my rucksack."

"So what?"

"Just thought you might like to share it."

"I'm not that sort of a girl, thank you very much!"

"I only meant if it got cold on the hill. . . ."

The crocodile whispered through a dead village. A car, a Jaguar, had buried its nose into the wall of a sharp corner and had been abandoned to the night. The crocodile stopped and gathered round the car and mourned its broken beauty.

"If I'd got a car like this I wouldn't run it into a wall."

"He must have been traveling."

"Bet it was a woman."

"A woman would've got round the corner. Women are more careful than men."

"Is that why you won't share my blanket?"

"Don't you ever think of anything else?"

"I'm having a Jag one day."

"Go on! What are you going to use for money— buttons?"

"Come on, you lot. It'll be daylight before we get there."

The crocodile stumbled and cursed up the hill, trapped and tormented by the darkness. The hill was large and steep and rough and crossed by dry stone walls, invisible in the night. The crocodile bruised its knees and laddered its nylons and wished it had stayed at home.

Midnight. Bodies heaped on a strange hill. Darkness on the cold earth. Hard rucksacks for pillows. Immoral bulges under a secret blanket. Shivering into slight sleep. A young Minister, new to his collar, reading a sermon he didn't understand to people who didn't want to listen. And a feeble hymn.

The snail of a night crawled toward morning.

A wash of slow light crept over the horizon, stained the eastern sky, wet the edges of the retreating night. The sun hid behind a pink rag of cloud. The hill stirred, tasted the morning, and shivered into waking. A prayer was muttered to the young, struggling day, a prayer to God's weekly miracle. Sunday. Give us this day, and the other six won't matter.

A girl said, "Look at my hair! I look a mess!"

And her boy friend replied, through a mouthful of sandwich, "You always look a mess."

Such is the gallantry of the very early morning.

The moors pitched and rolled like a petrified sea, deep and hard. The sun peeped over the edge of its cloud and saw the dismal, desolate world and vanished again.

The station at Edale, and the warm morning train, were a thousand cold, blistered miles away.

❋   ❋   ❋

"We'll miss the train!" wailed Maureen.

"It's only quarter past six," said Tony. "It doesn't go till half past."

The crocodile of the night before had broken and was stretched over a mile of Derbyshire. The sun had shrugged off its cloud, and the day eased into warmth.

Dots of hikers appeared on the rim of a distant valley and were etched for a moment against the vast, aching sky.

"Look how far they are in front," said Maureen.

"We'll never catch them," I said. "Anyway, my feet are dropping off."

"The train'll wait. They know we're coming so they'll wait," said Tony.

❀   ❀   ❀

Edale Station was a toy on the floor of the valley, and a toy train steamed and puffed at the platform. The doors were open and hikers were climbing inside, and one by one the doors were closing again.

"Come on! Come on!" yelled Maureen. "It's going!" We scrambled and fell down the steep valley sides and waved our frantic arms.

The train puffed a circle of smoke into the thin air, then another, and the train slowly left the toy station and puffed into the strange, quiet morning. The sound of the train bounced from the sides of the valley and was funneled into the solemn freedom of the sky. The world was sound in the sky and steam and a toy train vanishing into a new Sunday morning without us.

❀   ❀   ❀

The organ dirged around the prim, Sunday walls of the chapel. The congregation rustled and whispered and the golden evening was thwarted by the grim, high windows.

"Missed the train, didn't you?" said Max.

"Yes."

"What are you yawning for?"

"Didn't get back till three this afternoon. They don't run many trains on Sunday."

"You must be mad."

"I know that now."

The choir filed into their places, higher than the rest of us. The organ music rose to the ceiling and was trapped. The chapel coughed into silence. In the darkness of his robes, the Minister entered, like a black crow. His head was full of a secret God and he was waiting to strike his usual Sabbath bargain: empty hymns in exchange for a glimpse inside his head.

The hymns were chanted, the lesson read, the sermon, arid and brittle, was preached. The cringing collection plate begged along the pews like a persistent cripple.

But I chanted no hymns, nor ate the lesson, nor drank the sermon; and the begging collection plate passed untouched over my ungenerous knees.

I had fallen asleep on the hard, narrow pew.

10

Illuminations

"Packet of envelopes, please. Large size."

"I don't know what it's called but it's about this man who goes spying in Russia."

"Do you sell bootlaces?"

"We bought this yesterday, and it's broke."

"You haven't a very good selection, have you?"

"Only he's really a Russian spy pretending to be an English spy spying in Russia."

"Well, we only dropped it once."

"Do you know where I can get some bootlaces? They're for my husband—his trousers won't keep up."

"The service in shops isn't like it was before the war, is it, Edie?"

"I think I'll go elsewhere."

"Then he changed his mind and spied for the English so the Russians shot him."

"If we can't have it changed we want our money back."

"No! No! Large size!"

"You should know what it's called—you work here."

The shop floated on waves of wet sound. Customers poked and prodded and picked up and put down. Women chatted together on the floor of the shop as though they were at their own front gates. Shopping bags swam through the sea of humans, and the high, cluttered counter was a rock against the tide of demand, demand, demand.

"Where are the Christmas cards, young man?"

"They aren't on sale yet, madam."

"Hear that, Ethel? Not on sale yet! Would you believe it!"

"Fancy!"

"It's only just October, madam."

"We'll go elsewhere. Come on, Ethel."

"Fancy!"

They flowed through the doorway, two offended drops of water, searching for Christmas in October.

"Your afternoon off, isn't it?" whispered Pat. "No, sir, it was ten shillings you gave me, not a pound. Yes, sir, I'm sure."

"Yes," I muttered.

"Going anywhere?"

"Blackpool. Off to see the lights. Hired a coach."

"Lucky devil!"

A coin tapped the counter. "Yes, miss?"

"I want a present for my boy friend."

"Had you anything in mind?"

"No."

"Oh. How about a wallet?"

"He's got one."

"A writing case?"

"He don't write."

"We've a large selection of books."

"He don't read either. That all you got?"

"Perhaps you'd like to look round?"

"No, you don't seem to have much. I think I'll go somewhere else."

I went behind the rock of the counter and watched the crowd ebbing through the dinnertime doorway, leaving shrimp pools of people clinging to the shelves. Soon the bus would be clattering through the autumn to Blackpool, away from jumbled shelves and stubborn, low-tide shrimp pools.

"Have you any cigarettes, young man?" said a woman bulging fatly fur-coated over the counter.

"No, madam. We're——"

"Why not?"

"We're not a tobacconist's, madam."

"This is W. H. Smith's, isn't it?"

"Yes, but——"

"Then you sell cigarettes. I got some the other day from a W. H. Smith stall on the station at Crewe."

"Yes——"

"Platform two. Right next to the Ladi—the conveniences. I was visiting my husband."

"Your husband?"

"We're divorced, you know, and he won't pay his alimony as regular as he should. Used to beat me something cruel."

"We're not a——"

"Nobody knows what I suffered in the hands of that man. Nobody. 'Specially when he'd been drinking. And now he won't pay his alimony regular, have to visit him to get it. 'Course, I got the kids."

"Of course."

"Not a fit and proper person to look after children. That's what the judge said. P'raps you saw it in the papers?"

"No, madam."

"In all the Sundays. You married?"

"Not yet, madam."

"Well, when you are, treat your wife proper. Don't make her suffer like I suffered. And pay your alimony regular like a gentleman."

"I'll remember that, madam."

"I thought he was a gentleman. You wouldn't believe the way he changed after we married. Even on our wedding night—no, p'raps I'd better not say. You haven't any cigarettes, then?"

"I'm afraid not, madam."

"You should have; they had plenty at Crewe. A little consideration for your customers, that's all you need. My husband never had any consideration. I thought he had but he hadn't. . . ."

Sometimes the tide of demand throws up a whale or a swordfish or a shark, and in their loneliness they feed on shop assistants.

❧   ❧   ❧

October Blackpool. A sullenness of sea and sand. A blackness of raincoats. A stacking of deck chairs. A desertion of ice-cream stalls. Cold memories. Gray, wet gaiety.

The sea pushed with dull anger against the intruding land, and fat, black clouds brooded over the town. Light bulbs, like the many eyes of corpses, were stretched on wires slung between avenues of lamp posts. Yellow, squared lights, the windows of secret homes, were openings in the shuttered evening. The Tower raised its steel bones to the heavy sky, searching for a hidden, remembered sun.

Slowly and sadly, it began to rain.

Only the whining, blaring, violent fun fair raised two defiant fingers of light and noise at the undertakers of autumn. Only the fun fair clung to the memory of a washed-away holiday.

"Roll up! Win a coconut! Three throws for sixpence! You, sir! You look a strong chap. . . ."

"See the only three-headed cow in the world! Only half a crown for the sight of your life...."

"You've never seen the Dance of the Seven Veils performed like this before! Salome wasn't as daring as Suzie...."

Music blared to the sky, and the rain melted in the furnace of the deafening fun fair.

"Let's go on the Big Dipper!" I shouted into Ann's ear.

"I'm frightened!"

"I'll hold you!"

"That's what I'm frightened of!"

The Big Dipper roared and shuddered and thundered. The carriages whipped through a long tunnel at ground level, then climbed and plunged and climbed again until men left their seats and girls clung to their skirts and shrieked.

"Two, please," I said to the lever-pulling man in the control box.

"Five shillings."

I slid two half-crowns, half the contents of my pocket, toward him.

"Five shillings each," he said.

We climbed into a carriage, a trembling girl and a fat-faced destitute youth.

"Does that man control these things?" said Ann.

"No, he sends telegrams to the next-of-kin. That's why he needs so much money!"

The carriage jerked and gathered speed and shot into the tunnel. There was a small shriek, and two soft arms sprang around my neck and a soft face buried itself against my shoulder. The tunnel was long and dark, and we went through it twice.

❋   ❋   ❋

We dripped into the zoo in the Tower. Animals chattered and squeaked and coughed their lives away in small, barred worlds, smelling of stale jungles. A monkey swung endlessly through an artificial tree with three branches, and a lion slept nobly on dirty straw.

"I wish they'd feed the lions. I like to see that."

"Stick your arm through the cage. That'll feed 'em."

"Zoos always make me feel sick."

"Look in this cage. Reminds me of a meeting of the chapel Sisterhood."

"My mother happens to be the president of the Sisterhood!"

"Oh. Very sorry."

"I feel sick. It's this smell."

"You ought to be used to it—you came all the way from Rotherham on a bus with us."

"We'll take her outside, it's fresh air she needs."

The girls consoled each other through the doorway into the sad rain, and we found a bar that was crowded and dim and open.

The barmaid slid toward us like a pint of gin with bad feet.

"What can I do for you?" she said.

"Lots of things, precious."

"That'll do! You're too young to get fresh. Come to that, how old are you? Old enough to be in here?"

" 'Course. We're all eighteen. We were all eighteen yesterday."

"All on the same day?"

"Yes. Don't you believe us?"

"Oh, yes, oh, yes. I believe you like I believe we're in the middle of a heat wave. What do you want to drink?"

We placed our orders, letting the strange names trip off our tongues with proud, toddling maturity.

"I hope you can pay for this lot," said the barmaid.

" 'Course we can. Didn't we tell you?"

"Tell me what?"

"We won the Pools last week."

"Really. I married a prince last week."

"You'll be a princess, then. Where's your crown?"

"Same place as your Pools money."

"Well, we would've won, only Blackpool let us down. We had 'em for a draw and they lost, seven—one."

We spilled money onto the bar and swaggered manfully into the secret evening. The illuminations had been switched on.

❋ ❋ ❋

The coach crawled through an electric fairyland. Lights arched and pulsed over the promenade, making a tunnel for the gaping traffic. Two battleships, invisible in the day, fired light bulbs at each other, and glass flowers bloomed and burst on fields of darkness. A Noah's Ark beamed and waved under the hot arches, and the night hung wreaths of flame on the coffin of the dead town.

The warm, dark coach slid past carnival people staring at the lights and the wheels of the coach splashed trouser legs and the hems of coats, but nobody cared in the burning night.

Wonder sat in every seat.

"Look! There's an alligator waving its tail."

"And a bear dancing!"

"Wonder how they get them to go on and off like that?"

"A chap works the switches."

"They'd be in a right mess if the meter for this lot suddenly needed a shilling."

"One of those boats is sinking!"

"Women and children first!"

"Don't shout like that. People are looking."

"Isn't it lovely!"

"What happens if a fuse blows?"

"That light isn't very bright."

"That's a gas lamp, idiot!"

"It's like rainbows fighting one another."

"Go on! Fancy yourself as a poet, then?"

"Pity we have to go back to mucky Rotherham after this."

The coach shook off the clinging town, left it cremating on a brilliant horizon. Silence closed around, and each seat was a privacy of hope.

Ann dropped her head onto my shoulder and whispered, "Know what I liked best about today?"

"No. What?"

"The tunnel on the Big Dipper."

My arm slid round her, and the coach roared endlessly through the promised kingdom of the night, rattled and whispered into the darkness.

11

Eighteen Years

The door of the shop closed behind me, and I stepped into a street of shops, into the breathing November dusk. The windows of the shops were eyes in the face of the evening, the cold eye of the fishmongers, unfriendly as ice, the smoky eye of the tobacconists, the bloodshot bleary eye of the Effingham Arms, and the crossed eye of the opticians, they all looked at the evening, waited for the night. And some windows were trimmed with cotton-wool snow, and the eyes of these windows were looking for Christmas.

For Christmas was on the threshold of the world, trembling on the doorstep, sticking a cautious toe in the doorway which was edging open, wider and wider.

But Christmas hadn't yet touched the faces of the beaten people worrying past into their unknown evening, grim with living, sad with the future. One morning, too late, they would look up and see the tail of Christmas vanishing round the corner of the New Year, and they would shake their heads, swallow two aspirins, kick the crawling kids out of the way, and moan, "Christmas isn't as good as it used to be!" But not yet, for Christmas had still to touch them.

I wanted Christmas, I, with my shop-manager future, wanted people to climb onto my counter, shouting that we had no suitable cards and could they change the present they bought yesterday because little Arnold already had one? And I wanted them to ask what they could get for an old man of ninety-three who didn't smoke or drink and thought reading books sinful, and had we seen young Susan, she'd been here a minute ago, wearing a green coat and a knitted hat with a pompom on it? I wanted to be trampled on the mad Christmas Eve of bad memories.

I needed Christmas, and all the blind worriers could wrap their Christmases in holly paper, tie them with red string, and take them into a drafty corner and open them alone.

But this Christmas would be followed by my National Service. The army, and a two-year break from my career.

Ted was in the army. I remembered the morning of his going. The bedroom was tousled with the night and

Ted was in his best suit, brushed and creased, shoes glowing painfully, and his suitcase stood strangely on the floor.

"I'm off, then," he said.

"Off where?" It was early and my eyes were still heavy with sleep.

"The army. I'm off in the army."

"Oh." I made an effort and opened my eyes. "Righto, General. Don't do anything I wouldn't do."

"That gives me plenty of scope." He looked through the window, but his eyes didn't see the garden, they saw his childhood, and he didn't want to leave. He squared his brushed shoulders, picked up his suitcase, and marched into manhood. I was asleep before he reached the bottom of the stairs.

And now he was coming home on leave, home in his grim khaki and a bag over his shoulder and hands that had actually fired a rifle.

"My brother's coming home," I whispered to the worriers, but they didn't hear.

"My brother's coming, so is Christmas." But they were deaf, their ears blocked with the wax of worry.

Only the street heard; the cotton-wool, shopping-bag, many-eyed street heard and understood, and the understanding made it warm and secret, like a familiar fireplace on a rain-lashed night.

I went home, whistling. My head was aching, but

even a headache couldn't hurt the promise of the future and I whistled in spite of it.

❋   ❋   ❋

"How do you feel?" said the voice.

My sister loomed over me, a bottle in her hand.

"The top of my head keeps lifting off, and my throat is like sandpaper. Apart from that I feel fine."

"All this fuss over a bit of flu. I've brought your medicine."

"Who says it's flu?"

"The doctor, who else? Don't tell me you've forgotten; he came only yesterday. Says you'll be up by the weekend, so let's have no moaning how bad you are."

She poured the medicine into a spoon, carefully, without spilling a drop. The spoon advanced, then shrank to a burning dot of silver light.

"Come on! It's spilling!"

The dot swelled and was a spoon again.

"I felt a bit dizzy."

"You've been dizzy all your life. Drink this, I've got work to do."

She went, and the gray November window stabbed at my eyes. My head was a pincushion for hot needles of light, and my throat was tight, sore.

So the doctor had been. I couldn't remember. Flu. Lot of that about. Must be the weather. Soon be Christmas. Cotton-wool Christmas. I'll be up at the weekend. Back at work on Monday. A rest'll do me good. Wish my head didn't hurt so much. Soon be back at that chanting chapel with my friends. Ted's coming home. Walking down a street laughing at worried faces. Where? I know. The street told me Christmas was coming. All those windows like eyes. Wonder what those people were worrying about? They ought to smile more. Smile. I'm going to be a shop manager. Up at the weekend. God! I wish my bloody head didn't hurt. . . .

*   *   *

The book blurred and my eyes watered. Pity, I was enjoying it. Alexander Baron's *There's No Home.* A war story. Wish I'd fought in the war. No, I don't. Might've been killed. Wouldn't like to die. Not at eighteen with the world waiting. Wonder why I'm panting? Must be stuffy in here. Wish I was back on that coach coming from Blackpool. There was an outing for you. All those lights. Light. That window's burning my eyes, squeezing my head until my brain oozes through my ears. Draw the curtains 'cross that hurting window. This book's getting heavy. Look, my arm's dropping, can't hold it any more. Wonder why? Must have flu in my elbows. Ha! Flu in my elbows! Must remember that. Hello, Dad. Not too bad. I know I'm panting, can't do anything about that. My feet are hurting, too. Take the blankets off 'em. Blankets heavy on my feet, Dad. Tried to kick 'em off but they're too heavy. That's better. We'll have to get lighter blankets, Dad. These are made of lead. Dad, Dad, I've got flu in my elbows. . . .

❋   ❋   ❋

The ceiling pressed on my chest, and someone had taken the air from the room. My ears listened to the rasp and struggle of my lungs and the hammer of my heart. Can't breathe without air. Can't live without air.

"Doctor . . . Doctor. . . ."

"All right, Peter. We'll soon have you better."

Glad you're here, Doctor. Wouldn't like to die of flu. That's not very exciting. Sooner be killed in a war. Why are you tapping my knees, Doctor? Want me to kick my leg? Anything to oblige. Oops! Won't kick. Must have flu in my knees as well. Flu in my knees and elbows. There's a thing. Mustn't get flu in my you-know-what. Never be able to get married if I do. Come tomorrow, Doctor, I'll kick my leg for you tomorrow. Not today. Too tired today. Doctor, I can't breathe. Somebody's put the ceiling on my chest. Silly place to put a ceiling. Might hurt somebody. Might kill somebody. Might kill me. Doctor, I can't breathe, Doctor. . . .

"Peter, I'm going to send you into hospital for a wee while. They'll soon put you right."

Hospital? Can't do that, Doctor. I'm getting up at the

95

weekend. Going to work on Monday. Going to sell Christmas cards. Sell more Christmas cards than ever before. Going to sell the world as a Christmas card. Would you like the world to drop through your letter box, Doctor? Can't go in hospital. Can't breathe, listen at my heart. It'll come through my chest in a minute. Can't die of flu, Doctor. Not dignified. Everybody'd laugh. And he mounted to heaven on a flu germ. Hear about that lad? Died of flu. Tragic but funny. Oh Christ! Oh Christ! Oh Christ! What the bloody hell is wrong with me . . . ?

*　　　*　　　*

The room waited. The heavy tick of the clock, solemn on the wall, was the only sound. The curtains shut out the night, made a hidden cave of the room. Four people were there: a woman, seated, her shoulders in the circle of her husband's arm; an old man with new lines cutting his face; a young man in the uniform of a soldier. And they didn't look at one another but at the carpet, the walls or the ticking, solemn clock. They were alone in the evening; even together, each was alone. They were waiting for the doctor who was upstairs.

Footsteps sounded on the stairs, and a door opened. The doctor entered the room. He was a big man, big with the pain of his work, and his eyebrows were gray though his hair was black. He looked at the waiting people. And he said:

"I'm afraid it's polio."

There was no sound, only the tick of the clock, stuttering into the night, into the dark night.

12

In

The corners of the ward were shadowed; black shadows which bruised the edge of the light thrown by the single globe in the center of the never-ending ceiling.

Eight beds marched down one side of the ward and facing them were eight squat-legged boxes like coffins. They were iron lungs. The light splashed nervously over their grim, cold wood. Seven of the beds and all the iron lungs were empty, unwanted.

But the eighth bed wasn't empty; on it a youth writhed under a thin, white sheet, and grouped round it were several gowned figures: doctors and nurses. One of the nurses leaned forward and sponged the youth's face and neck. She was young, like the youth on the bed, and she wondered if she were about to witness her first death and whether she would faint if she did.

To the youth, the ward was a tunnel with its ceiling

lowering and its sides closing in. And the single globe of light was a scalding sun that had shriveled the air in the tunnel until each breath was a task that was never completed. His sun, the light, whirled and shrank and swelled and his body was a map of pain. He had a lucid thought that didn't live in the swirling light and pain: like the nurse, he wondered if he were about to witness his first death.

Voices in the hollow ward were swallowed by the shadows.

"Sponge, Nurse."

"How is he now?"

"Total paralysis of legs, trunk, and arms. Extreme difficulty with his breathing. Still delirious."

"Iron lung?"

"Only as a very last resort."

"Sponge again, Nurse."

Above the stubble of beard on the youth's face his eyes were clenched against the light, and his cheeks were sharp and white.

And thoughts rattled round his head, peas in a bleached skull:

Christ. . . . No air. . . . Bloody funny flu. . . . We opened the window and influenza. . . . Lovely girl, enza. . . . Turn that light . . . off . . . off. . . . Worse than Blackpool. . . . Ha! visit the lights . . . in my head . . . miles of 'em. . . . God! It hurts . . . it hurts. . . .

One of the gowned ghosts said: "The light seems to

be bothering him. Can we dim it?" Another ghost touched a switch on the wall, and the light shrank and the bruising shadows edged closer.

What're you doing . . . with my legs. . . . Don't bend 'em up, you fools . . . straighten 'em. . . . You're breaking . . . my back. . . .

"Your legs are straight, Peter. Perfectly straight."

Liar . . . bloody liar. . . . I can feel 'em . . . bending. . . .

"We'll soon have you better."

Is it Christmas . . . yet? . . . Merry Christmas one . . . and all. . . . Have a cigar. . . . Wrong . . . what's wrong with . . . me . . . ?

One of the ghosts glanced at the others, then bent over the shouting youth on the bed.

"You have polio, Peter," he said. "Are you worried?"

Worried? . . . it's a bloody relief. . . . I thought it was . . . flu. . . .

The light danced and whirled and twisted inside his head, burned like acid into his brain and the corner shadows swelled toward the light.

❋   ❋   ❋

It was another day; another evening dusked through the tall windows behind the beds. A nurse looked down at the youth. His eyes were closed, and his cheeks were sharper, thinner. His beard was losing its coarseness, becoming softer. The nurse was about to turn away when he opened his eyes.

She said, "I thought you were asleep. There's some visitors for you."

She turned the bed round until he could see through one of the tall windows. A man and a youth in soldier's uniform were outside, looking in.

Hello, Dad . . . hello, Ted. . . . What're you doing out there. . . . Scared of catching something . . . ? Can't hear a word you're saying. . . . You look like fish through that glass. . . . No, I can't talk . . . not enough air . . . some idiots've pinched it. . . . Bit of a hindrance to fluent conversation, not being able to talk. . . . You look cold. . . . I'm not . . . sweating like a pig. . . . Can't lift my arm . . . don't know why. . . . Yes, I do! I remember. . . . Dad, I've got polio, Dad. . . . Polio . . . isn't that nice . . . ? Never had that before. . . . Try anything once. . . . No air in here, it's like drowning . . . without water. . . . Dry drowning. . . . I'll open a chain of dry-drowning shops . . . like dry cleaners. . . . Come to Marshall's. Neater-Quicker-Cleaner. . . . Special rates for your mother-in-law. . . . Wonder what it's like, polio? Can't breathe. . . . Oh Christ! Oh Christ! Oh Christ . . . ! Send 'em away, Nurse . . . send 'em away. . . .

A nurse spoke to the two visitors. They listened as if they didn't believe, then turned and walked into the deep evening.

✿   ✿   ✿

Another night stained the corners with shadows. A single light glared above the bed. White-gowned figures looked down at the youth. His eyes had black circles round them, and they were screwed shut as though he wanted to see inside himself. His neck was rigid under an invisible strain. His breathing was very shallow, and there was a rasp with each indrawn breath. His beard curved silkily round his thin face.

The gowned figures lifted him, carried him toward the iron lungs.

He opened his eyes and tried to speak, but no sound came. He seemed frightened. An arm dropped and swung downward like a dead arm. A nurse placed it gently across his chest, twisting the fingers with the fingers of the other hand to prevent it falling again.

They placed him in an iron lung, locked an arch of wood across his neck. Only his head was visible, and his eyes were wide and scared. A switch was pressed, and the ward was filled with the deep, even breathing sound of the lung.

The youth's eyes lost their wide fear; they seemed surprised, then pleased. A smile spread slowly over his sweaty, bearded face.

13

Out

"It was a marvelous feeling," said my head.

"You had the widest smile of relief I've ever seen," said the nurse.

"It was like a twenty-stone man getting off my chest. What's your name?"

"Nurse."

"That isn't a name, it's a condition."

She said: "It's Pat, but you mustn't call me that when Sister's around."

"Why?"

"Because that's why. How do you find the lung?"

"Well, it's nice to breathe again. How does it work?"

"You would ask me that. It pumps air over you which presses down your chest, then sucks the air out, leaving a vacuum which lets your chest expand. I think."

"It works, anyway," I said. "How long have I been in it?"

"One night. Don't you remember?"

"Not very well. I can remember being in bed at home. Then an ambulance. Being undressed in here, having a needle stuck in my back——"

"That was a lumbar puncture."

"After that it's blurred. I remember the pain."

"You were delirious," she said. "You cursed at everybody, including the Superintendent."

"I did?"

"Yes. Called him a so-and-so liar."

"That isn't swearing."

"You didn't say so-and-so. Like a drink?"

"Yes, please."

She held a cup against my cheek and put the end of a straw between my lips.

"Swallow only when the lung's breathing in," she said.

"Why?"

"You might choke. Nobody can swallow when they're breathing out, and the lung's doing your breathing for you."

"You've put me off my drink now."

"Take it slowly," she said. "You'll get the hang of it."

I took the drink in slow sips while my eyes wandered through the limited field of vision: the pale green upper wall, half a window, the cracked ceiling, the upside-down, serious face of the nurse.

In the lung, under the rushing, retreating air, I tried to lift my arm. Nothing happened. Then my legs. Again, nothing. Not even my fingers and toes. The arch of wood across my neck divided my head from my body, the living from the frozen. I was in two pieces, and it was funny because I'd been one a week ago. Now I was divorced.

"Why the grin?" asked Pat.

"Struck me as funny."

"What did?"

"My head's divorced my body. They couldn't get on together."

She looked at her feet and shuffled them a little. Her end of the straw came out of the cup, and she fumbled it back in without looking at me.

"What's wrong, Pat?" I said.

"We don't address our nurses by their first names," a new voice said, and another face floated above mine. A face with a mouth that curved upward toward laughter and eyes that were kind and Irish.

"I'm the Sister," said the face. "You've seen me before, but you weren't in a condition to notice. How are you?"

"Fine, thanks."

"Good, good." She patted the top of the iron lung. "Now we'll have to see about getting you out of this thing."

"Out? I've only just got in."

"I know, but you don't want to stay there forever, do you?"

This was new; this was the future touching a mind still recovering from the past. How could I get out of the lung? I couldn't breathe out there. Perhaps they'd forgotten to tell the Sister.

"The sooner we get you out of here," she said, "the sooner we can get you walking."

"Get you walking." What did she mean, "Get you walking?" I could walk. I walked to work the other week. Through Clifton Park where we used to fly our airplanes. And now the world had shrunk into a breathing box, and a mad woman was nattering about walking again as though I was a cripple or something.

The Sister turned and walked down the long, empty ward. My mind tried to hold the future, but it was greasy and it kept slithering away. A week ago—was it only a week?—my life had been ordered, normal, traveling on safe lines in a known direction. Now the lines had vanished, the direction wasn't known. Unless all this was a nightmare, a daymare, a new kind of dream in which the dreamer dreamed without sleeping. No, it was happening; my limbs wouldn't move, and I couldn't breathe outside this strange box. That was real enough. But it wouldn't last, it couldn't last. One day the box would vanish, my limbs would unfreeze, and I would go home to my life with nothing but a few heroic memories. Of course it couldn't last.

The afternoon darkened into evening. The long ward was quiet and calm, like an empty church waiting for Sunday. I forgot the future and listened to the deep, regular breathing of the lung and was comforted by it.

❂   ❂   ❂

"They've disinfected the house," said Dot.

"What for?"

"Because of you," said Ted. "Infectious diseases and all that. I've got compassionate leave from the army."

"What for?" I said again.

"They always give you that when you've a relative who's dangerou——"

"This thing comfortable?" asked Dot and nudged Ted angrily when she thought I wasn't looking.

"Very," I said. "You look funny upside-down."

"I don't feel funny."

I said: "How're things at home?"

"Stinks of disinfectant."

"That'd better be gone when I get back."

They were wearing surgical masks, and their eyes above them avoided mine. Somebody was always avoiding my eyes.

I said: "I think I'll buy a new bike. The exercise'll do my legs good. They'll probably be a bit weak at first."

Dot stood up and walked swiftly down the ward into the kitchen. Ted shuffled his invisible feet and tried to think of something to say. I closed my eyes and thought: A Raleigh like that one in Siddall's window. Wonder if it'll still be there when I get out? I'll be able to go to all the old places, Blyth, Roche Abbey, even the coast when I'm stronger. I opened my eyes and saw Dot's face above mine. Her eyes above the surgical mask were red and damp.

I said: "Dot, why've you been crying?"

*   *   *

It wasn't real; it was endless drowning under a pool of air, straining for the surface, for breath, for life. Deeper, deeper, deeper, while the faces above me swam and dissolved and leered; while the ceiling blurred and blackened, and a voice that didn't belong to me but was my own, rattled, "Put me back, put me back. . . ."

Down under the drowning air, under the mocking normal world into an airless cave, and the faces and the dark ceiling swelled and disappeared forever and the rattling voice croaked, "Put me . . ." and was silent in an unreal eternity. . . .

And then the air was rushing and retreating over my body. My chest filled. The faces above me wavered into focus. The ceiling was light again. I was back in the iron lung.

"What happened?" I said.

"You passed out," said the Sister. "Don't worry about it." She smiled her quick Irish smile and bustled down the ward.

Pat cleared the breakfast debris from my locker top and said, "How do you feel?"

"Better now I'm in here. Have I got to go through that again?"

" 'Fraid so."

"Hope you don't keep me out as long next time, then."

She picked up her tray and said, "You were out for exactly two minutes. We timed you." She walked down the ward, and the cup and the plate on the tray clattered into the kitchen.

*   *   *

The days developed a pattern: the slow awakening to the same dawn; the breakfast eggs with six bread fingers; the bucket-clatter of cleaning women in the growing light; Sister's smiling greeting; the blank morning; the nurse who fed me with my dinner, holding the plate in one hand and the jabbing fork in the other; the blank afternoon; the doctor's round—"Hello, old chap, how are you today?" "Fine, thanks, Doctor." "Good, good."—supper, soup and something else; the strange half-hour visiting time; the blank evening. This was the pattern of the days.

And through the pattern, woven like a thread of hot

wire, was the time spent outside the lung, the dreaded, drowning time. A little more each day, painful minutes squeezed from my trampled lungs. Oh, it was so easy in the box and so hard out.

I learned the trick of not looking into the future; of not looking beyond the next meal so that when it arrived I had reached a point in time and was satisfied. It was like the trick I had when cycling, of not looking beyond the next milestone. That way it was a surprise to be home. I knew the long months were waiting so I ignored them.

And sometimes there was an alien thread on the pattern of the days. A thread that needed to be picked up and closely examined: a visit from the chapel Minister. He came once when I had been out of the lung for an hour and was near my sweating limit. I couldn't speak, but I could think.

"Hello, Peter," he said. "Oh, I forgot. Sister said you mightn't be able to speak. Don't worry, leave the talking to me."

And he was silent, stuck for words. Then, "Rotherham lost on Saturday. You'll have to come to Newcastle, see a decent football team."

You Geordies are all alike. Half of you don't know a football from an egg.

"We held a special service for you. The chapel was packed. Wish I could get that many every Sunday."

We can't all be popular.

"Everyone asks about you, even people who don't know you. Somebody's always stopping me. Would you like me to wipe your face, you're sweating."

That's the lack of air. Somebody's pinched it.

"The Youth Club send their best wishes. They say the place doesn't seem the same without you."

Wipe my face, then, if you're going to.

"Well, I shall have to go. I'll come again as soon as I'm able. Shall we say a prayer before I go?"

He clasped his hands together and closed his eyes. His head was bowed, his face hidden. I wanted to tell him not to bother, that words were only words, without a past or future. Just pegs for our use and if there wasn't anything to hang on them, it wasn't much use nailing them up. It was the first time I had realized that, and I was surprised with myself.

"Almighty Father," he said, "in Thy wisdom and mercy, help this boy regain his strength. . . ."

He came several times, and he always said a prayer. That was his work, his vocation. It was my work to find the truth behind his lonely, screening words. And to understand it.

✿   ✿   ✿

A new name whispered its way into my life. A nurse said, "When you get out of this lung you'll be able to go to King Edward's." My visitors said, "Have you heard about King Edward's?" A white-coated woman came

111

and lifted and twisted my dead legs until they burned. "I'm the physiotherapist from King Edward's," she said.

I asked and was told, "King Edward's? That's the Orthopedic Hospital. You'll go there when you can manage without this lung."

"What's it like?"

"Nice. They've got a pool down there to exercise you in. And a gymnasium. They can do wonders down there with chaps like you."

Chaps like me? Wonders? What was so wonderful about walking again? And why "Chaps like me"? I wasn't any different to anybody else except that I'd been ill and now couldn't move for some queer medical reason. But that was only temporary. Wasn't it?

One hour; two; two and a half; three; five hours, fifteen minutes. Slowly and silently I fought the lung through the long days and tired nights. November edged into December. I graduated to lying on an ordinary bed when I was out of the lung and knew that I was winning. Six hours, seven. Breakfast until supper. Nurses decorated the ward with red lanterns and Christmas cards began to arrive in the morning post. Ten hours. Ten hours of tight, shallow, sometimes difficult, breathing. Then the clinging relief of the lung.

The fingers of my left hand began to move.

I watched their weak bending as if they belonged to somebody else. But they were mine, and they were moving. Christmas cards arrived with every post, and streamers joined the lanterns on the celebrating ceiling. The world outside was cold, and my visitors brought small fogs on their breath and wondered if it would snow. But my world was small and warm, and it was covered with cards and lanterns and streamers. I didn't envy my visitors.

A week before Christmas I stayed out of the lung for twenty-four hours. A day and a night. Breakfast until breakfast until breakfast.

The iron lung glared at me, its black mouth wide with anger, helpless on its splayed legs. I couldn't move, but I could breathe. Each breath, each mouthful of air, was my own, sucked into my chest by myself and blown out by myself. I could breathe.

Whisper it carefully, whisper it in Rotherham, in Clifton Park, in the cabbage halls of Oakwood; whisper it in the grimness of the chapel: Peter can breathe. Mr. Marshall no longer requires his iron lung. That lad's gettin' better. But whisper it carefully, it might only be a dream.

The doctor said, "Good, good, good. Shall we burn this lung now?" And he grinned.

"Yes," I said, "I shan't need it any more." And we laughed at nothing. Sister came and laughed with us. I sucked in my own air and blew it out again, felt my chest rising and falling, felt the weak muscles expanding.

Oh, what a morning it was!

A cold sun fingered the red lanterns and swooping streamers, and the ward glittered with the coming Christmas. Nurses came and went like blue-and-white shadows. The dinner arrived at the kitchen. The hands of the clock on the wall prayed over the black, chipped twelve. A nurse brought in a plate and began feeding me. I moved the fingers of my left hand secretly under the blankets.

My second life was a morning old.

❋   ❋   ❋

Seventy-two Christmas cards were taped to the wall behind my head where I couldn't see them. But I knew they were there, and I knew what they were like: holly and snow and stage coaches; cardboard robins and silent bells and shouting boys sliding on the ice of another century and little girls with wind-red cheeks and holy eyes; and somber saints frowning from the tower of their goodness on the guilty gaiety of the other cards. Christmas trapped on a wall.

Christmas Eve. Seven nurses, red-cloaked and pure with the night, sang their lantern-lit way through the wards of the hospital. Their voices were strained and tired when they reached me.

"Is there any special carol you'd like?" they asked.

"Silent Night." It was the first thing that came into my head.

They sang:

Silent Night, Holy Night,
All is calm, all is bright,
Round yon virgin

—a giggle, a blush, an angry nudge—

Mother and Child,
Holy infant, so tender and mild. . . .

I could bend my left wrist a little, and my fingers could almost touch the palm of my hand. But the rest of me was dead. Soon I would be going to a wonder-working hospital, then home and the beautiful song of this cloaked choir would be just another memory.

A card slipped off the wall and drifted like a strayed snowflake onto the pillow beside my head. From the edge of my eye, I saw that it was a religious one: a badly drawn baby squinting at the shining head of its mother and a cow gaping holily at them both.

The carol reached a ragged end, and the choir Merry Christmased its way out of the ward. I was alone with the unique night and my dead body and the memories of the eves of my other Christmases:

A nut-shell-littered hearth and a tree in the corner on the box where the wireless usually stood. Brothers and aunts and cousins and my father bribing us to bed with a toy. The determination to stay awake and the weight of sleep on grimly open eyes. The promise of the morning and the certainty that there would be snow on the ground when we awoke. Warm laughter downstairs. The Christmas Eves of childhood that are never forgotten and never known again.

And the Christmas Eves of my youth. The party at the chapel. The arguments under the mistletoe. And the midnight carol service when the chapel was beautiful with song and a once a year reality, and the whole world was starting again. Frosty lips at a secret gateway and the walk home through the magic streets. . . .

Now other children were climbing other stairs and chapels that I didn't know were alive with song. My bed was my stairs and my body was its own chapel and my Christmas was on a pale green wall, out of my reach.

❖   ❖   ❖

Early in the New Year, Sister said: "The ambulance is coming in the morning, Peter."

"Ambulance? What ambulance?"

"To take you to King Edward's."

"Oh. The potato palace. At last."

She said, "Potato palace?"

"King Edward's."

She laughed down the ward and into the kitchen.

I put out my tongue at the iron lung and said, "I've licked you, you gaping device. Thanks."

I thought it was over, but it wasn't.

14

The Ambulance Ride

Sister said: "Remember, Peter. It's a case of mind over mattress."

"Don't worry, Sister. I'll be back to dance with you."

"Sure, an' I'll look forward to that."

The ambulance men wheeled my stretcher across the yard toward their vehicle. Sister stood on the steps and waved. The January air was as sharp as frost, and the sky moving over my face was a thin, sweet blue.

We jolted through the gates of the hospital and into the world. Nothing had altered in the last three months: the houses were the same, and the same people stooped round bus stops, frightened by the sun and the blue sky—the curve of their backs said that such things didn't ought to happen, not in January; sunshine was for August, snow and slush for January, and where the hell was that bus?

And yet, nothing was the same. It was as if I was seeing everything for the first time, with the eyes of a new-born baby and the reasoning power of an adult. The houses were neater, cleaner, and there was poetry in the stooped shoulders of the people.

But when I walked among them again that would vanish. When my eyes were used to them I wouldn't notice. And that would be soon.

I wanted to shout, to laugh, but there was an old nurse huddled like a crow in the corner of the ambulance. The lines on her face said that she didn't like shouting and laughter.

A man on a corner took off his hat as we passed as though we were a funeral. "I'm not dead," I chased him with my thoughts. "I can't move, but I'm not dead. Put your hat back on, you old fool."

The ambulance jerked down the steep hills, put a sweet illusion of movement into my body. The cap of the crow nurse slid over her eyes, and she pushed it back with an angry, bony claw of a hand. She spoke for the first and last time, "I'll be glad when today is over."

Perhaps her crow of a husband had flown to another nest, and she wanted to mourn him in the white sorrow of their once-crackling double bed. Perhaps she was a bat, not a crow.

The sky, through the dark glass of the window, was July-blue and empty. Empty? An empty sky. Three months since I last saw it, three months of visitors in masks, and sickness, and a high-roofed, echoing, lonely ward and eight grinning iron lungs. And a Minister praying to his own private piece of the empty sky.

"God moves in mysterious ways His wonders to perform" and all the other excuses just would not do. Man was an accident of evolution and the need for a religion for a convenient superior power onto whose shoulders he could pile the responsibility of his own weakness proved that the evolution was still continuing. And would do so until Man realized that he alone was responsible for his own destiny, that he needed only the religion of humanity and all the rest were growing pains. On that changing morning it tasted like the truth.

The ambulance stopped in a strange yard. The crow nurse pulled her cloak around her, stepped into the painful day and hopped away in search of the welcome sorrow of the night.

They wheeled me under the blue arch of my cool and never-to-be-forgotten January sky, through a doorway, under a narrow ceiling, down a corridor through the clatter of a thousand new sounds, into a small room, and there they lifted me onto a bed.

"Hello. I'm Eric," a voice said. "Welcome to the abbatoir."

"Hello. Is it as bad as that?"

"Not really. You'll like it here. The first five years are the worst."

The room was small and friendly. Flowered curtains were at the windows, and much of the sky was visible. Of course I would like it, they were going to work wonders with me, weren't they?

15

The Potato Palace

"Let's see what you can do with this hand," said the physiotherapist.

My left arm was suspended in a sling. I clenched my hand into a weak fist and swayed the wrist backwards and forwards.

"Good. Can you bend the arm?"

I bent the arm.

"Now straighten it."

I straightened. It wouldn't straighten. It hung there as though the muscle had been removed.

"It won't straighten," I said.

"Mmmm. Triceps not working. Biceps fair. Not uncommon in these cases." She pulled the blanket off my body. "Let's see what else you can—or can't—do."

For half an hour she poked and prodded, twisted and turned. But she didn't discover any movement. My right arm, left shoulder, stomach, back, and both legs were totally paralyzed.

I said, "What is polio, exactly?"

"It's a virus which prevents messages from the brain reaching the muscles. It does this by attacking the nerve cells controlling movement."

"What does it do to them?"

"It either knocks them out or kills them. If a nerve cell is knocked out it may recover, even fully. If it's killed it won't."

"And my nerve cells? Are they knocked out or killed?"

Our voices were low, disinterested almost. It might have been two people discussing the weather, this conversation about my body.

"We don't know yet," she said. "That's what we have to find out."

"How long will that take?"

"Anything up to two years. Like to see the pool?"

Two years. I would be twenty, nearly twenty-one. "Pool?"

"Where we exercise our customers."

She wheeled me into another room. I turned my head and saw a small swimming pool surrounded by a low wall. A stretcher was suspended from the ceiling on rails which ran to the edge of the room. People were in the pool, floating and hobbling. Eric stood stiffly in one corner, the water up to his shoulders. He called, "Come on in. It's better than Blackpool."

"Soon," said the physiotherapist behind me. "When you're a bit stronger we'll have you in."

She pushed me back to the dinnertime ward. Two years. My National Service in a hospital.

❋   ❋   ❋

Morning. Breakfast clattered in and out again. A chatter of nurses smoothed the bedsheets to an uncomfortable tightness.

"I'm getting engaged."

"Who to?"

"A lad."

"That's a novelty."

"Don't be saucy, I know somebody who didn't get engaged to a lad."

"Go on. Who?"

"My brother."

"He's buying me a ninety-three-pound ring."

"Does he know?"

"Not yet."

"What if he won't buy it?"

"Then I'll get engaged to somebody who will."

"Anyone want the tish wagon?"

"The what?" I said.

"It's the trolley they bring the bedpans on," said Eric.

"Why 'tish'?"

"You'll have to excuse the minds of these nurses. Turn the word round."

"Turn th—— Oh."

Later, I went to the Physiotherapy Department to have my arms and legs suspended in slings.

"Try to move what you can, Peter."

I tried to move my feet, but nothing happened. Perhaps they didn't belong to me. I looked round furtively for their owner, but there was nobody near me. They were mine. "Come on, feet. You used to belt a football pretty hard. All I want you to do now is waggle a bit." But they hung there like the feet of a statue; even the toes were as active as dead Guardsmen.

"What about the hands, Peter?"

"Come on, right hand, the left hand can do it. Watch!" The left hand clenched in obliging example to its mate. "Come on, now." But the message didn't get beyond the sleeping—or dead—nerve cells, and the fingers of the right hand drooped downward like petrified sausages.

I went back to the ward and the chattering nurses and Eric.

＊   ＊   ＊

Another day, and a new nurse in the ward. A fair-haired girl with a wide smile and serious green eyes. She said her name was Claire. She washed and dressed

124

me and helped lift me onto the trolley which was taking me to the Physiotherapy Department. When I came back she fed me with my dinner, then shaved me. During that afternoon, and the days that followed, we saw her smile, wide and friendly, and knew her kindness which came from inside her not from the uniform she wore. But I saw and knew something more, which I thought nobody else could see, but I was wrong.

"You're fond of Claire, aren't you?" said Kate, sticking a supper chip into my mouth.

" 'Course he is," said Eric. "Can't wait till she gets on duty."

"Ignore that old man," I said. "Is it that obvious?"

"Obvious! Ha!" Eric snorted. "You only talk about her in your sleep, that's all."

"If you don't belt up, I'll . . ."

"You'll what?"

"Get out of this bed and brain you."

"Don't do that. Not without your trousers on."

"When you two have finished," said Kate, "we'll get back to the subject under discussion." She stuck another chip in my mouth. "Shall I tell her?"

"Tell who what?"

"Don't speak with your mouth full," said Eric. "No manners, that's the trouble with the younger generation."

"Tell Claire that you're fond of her," said Kate.

125

"No! No! No!" I nearly choked on the chip.

"Why not?" said Eric. "Might be the start of something beautiful."

"I'll beautiful you if I come over there!"

"Now, now, now. No violence, please—this is a respectable establishment."

It was the late evening of a wind-torn March day. The sort of evening when the outside world didn't exist and the future was forgotten. Nothing mattered except this warm softly dark room and the excitement of a new dream. That's the sort of evening it was.

*   *   *

Claire stood in the cold, leaf-twisting, shrill morning doorway. Eric grinned slyly, and I kept my eyes closed.

"Peter."

"Yes?"

"Breakfast. Cornflakes or porridge?"

"Er—cornflakes, please."

She went, and Eric said, "She wants nowt to do with you. Don't blame her; if I were a girl I wouldn't either."

"If you were a girl I'd be happy to remain a bachelor."

Claire returned and began feeding me. I opened my eyes and saw that she was staring hard at the plate in her hand and her cheeks were pink. Nothing was said. Breakfast was cleared away. Patients were dressed.

Nurses came and went. It was time for the daily sling suspension, time to be dressed. Claire came to do the job.

And behind the flowered, friendly bed screens we forgot hospital ethics, and I knew it wasn't a dream any more.

      ❋   ❋   ❋

It was April. Claire was working on another ward. I hadn't seen her for weeks. "They'll always move 'em, just when we've got 'em trained," Eric said. Our beds were side by side. I was dictating a letter to Claire, Eric was writing it. Although we couldn't meet—the hospital powers-that-be assume that when a body is paralyzed, so also are the heart and mind—we wrote as often as possible.

"I'll blackmail you one of these days," said Eric. "Twenty thousand quid or I spill the beans to the Sunday papers."

"What are you babbling about?"

"The stuff you put in these letters. The Vicar wouldn't like it."

"The Vicar isn't going to get it. It raises problems, though."

"The only problem we have right now," he said, "is whether or not we'll get this letter finished before the weekend. It's Tuesday, already."

"Where are we up to?"

"I don't know. I lost count after page eight. What sort of problems?"

"Well, what happens if I don't walk again?"

He said, "Have they told you that?"

"They've hinted. I'm not a fool, I can add two and two. Only just, but I can do it."

"Wait till they tell you for certain," said Eric. "And remember, the problem hasn't been invented that can't be got round one way or another. Now let's get on with this scorching letter."

We lay side by side, like two men of long friendship in the padded leather armchairs of an exclusive club. But the ties that held us were stronger than the ties of school or regiment or profession. They were the ties of crippled bodies and helplessness and dependence on others. And with our joking and laughter we tattooed the skin of a large defeat with small victories.

16

The Threads

April. May.

"How's it going, Peter?"

"Left arm's getting stronger. They slung it in a sling yesterday so's I could feed myself with jam sandwiches."

"Nothing else?"

"No. Jam was all they had."

"I meant was there any more movement anywhere?"

"No. Nothing else."

With the coming of the fickle warmth of spring I went into the pool, swung on the stretcher above the water, above the floating, hobbling, polio-dead, spastic-twitching bodies of this cool, weightless muscular world.

They lowered the stretcher, and the water touched my heels, explored my legs, discovered my cotton-black trunks, swam up to my neck until only my head, on a cork pillow, was above the surface.

From his corner, Eric scooped water at me.

"Welcome, O Wondrous One, to the green waters of the Nile."

"It's better than Monte Carlo," I said.

"Ever been?"

"No, but I've been to Monte Cleethorpes."

The physiotherapist, in a black, slack, cotton costume, waded toward me.

"Look out, Miss World's coming," Eric whispered. "Behave yourself."

"Now, Peter," she beamed. "Let's see what you can do under water. Clench your fist."

I clenched my fist; I waggled my wrist; I bent my arm. The three movements I could perform on land. But they were the only ones: my right arm hung in the water like a dead fish, and my legs floated aimlessly, the toes poking through ten holes in the water like midget rocks at low tide.

"Water won't help you to move what you can't move," said the physiotherapist. "It just makes it easier to make what movement you can. Does away with gravity and so on. And if anything does come back in your right arm or your legs we'll detect it quicker in water than we would on land."

She wound the stretcher out of the water; I felt the

weight returning, pressing on me. The dead, heavy weight of my own body.

✱ ✱ ✱

The realization was a gradual thing; from the certain knowledge that the wonder-working King Edward's would effect a certain cure, I slid down the slow slope of reality, scrambling toward the dream but always slipping backward to the truth.

At first, I thought, "Soon life will return to my legs. Soon I'll be walking. Weak at first, of course, but strengthening all the time. And one day I'll walk to the ambulance, or even the bus, and go home. Home. Up the Crescent on my two legs, along the garden path, through the door as casually as if I hadn't been anywhere. And they'd be having their tea, and they'd look at me in amazement because I wouldn't tell 'em I was coming. And I'd say: 'What's for tea, then? I'm starving,' just like I used to when I came in from work."

Oh, what a day that will be!

And later, weeks later, "Of course, I might need a stick when I go home. Or crutches, even. Must face up to that. And irons on my legs. I wouldn't care for that very much, but it won't last forever. I'll exercise until I can throw the irons and crutches away. A walking stick wouldn't be so bad, a walking stick and a slight, but heroic, limp."

And near the bottom of the slope, "But if my arms won't move, how can I hold crutches or a stick? In my teeth? No irons, no crutches, no stick, no heroic limp, no strength. What then?"

And at the bottom of the slope, when I could slide no lower, "A wheel chair. Oh, what a day that will be."

I read the Bible, but it contained no answers. It wasn't meaningless. I could see the meaning, the need for Man to have a security outside his understanding, but was it better than any other Man gods, the sun, earth, air, fire, water? Didn't they serve the same purpose, to comfort Man until his knowledge was larger than his ignorance?

I searched the Bible, thinking I needed the convenience of a God, needing to know there was a somebody, something, who could restore my health and strength by snapping his, its, fingers. I thought I needed to know the reason for my being crippled at the age of eighteen, at the sweet beginning of life. Then I could spend my life looking for the reason, and, not finding it, say, "After death, in Heaven, I'll know why." But my life would be an excuse.

And if I accepted that it was an ironic accident in time and space, that I collided at the wrong moment with an invisible polio virus, a several million-to-one shot, then the future was mine, and my second life, a wet mass of shapeless clay, was mine to shape and mold and direct, and the answers would come from inside myself, not from the Bible, and the strengths and weaknesses, failures and successes of my new life were mine, and so was the hope. After death, in the grave, I would never know why.

I searched the Bible, but it hadn't the answers. They were inside myself, with the questions.

❋   ❋   ❋

It was a beautiful wheel chair. It had a dark-red back and seat. The chrome glistened like glass. There was a deep, brown, comfortable cushion to sit on. It was mine.

It was mine.

I wore a corset, into which I had been laced like a nineteenth-century chorus girl. It reached from my shoulders to my hips, and it had two groin straps which took a perverse delight in attempting to castrate me. "Your back isn't strong enough to let you sit up without it," they explained.

They lifted my rag-doll body and put it on the deep cushion.

"How's that?" they asked.

"Dunno, yet." I looked down at the chair. The big wheel on the right-hand side was minus a propelling ring. The left wheel had two, the outer one smaller than the inner.

"It's a one-wheel drive," they explained. "For people

133

with use in their left arms only. The outer ring is connected by a rod with the right-hand wheel. If you push that ring you'll turn to the right. Push the inner one and you'll turn to the left."

"What if I push them both together?"

"You'll go straight forward. Have a try."

I put my hand on the cold chrome rings but nothing happened. The chair might have been nailed to the floor.

I said, "There isn't any push in my arm."

"Mmmm. We were afraid of that. Triceps again. The same muscles that straighten the arm would be needed to push the wheel round. And they don't work, do they?"

"No. They don't work."

"Never mind, you can still be pushed where you want to go."

Never mind, never mind. Sit there in your mobile immobility, and never mind. You can still be pushed.

Later the same week two physiotherapists laced me into my chorus-girl corset, lifted me into my new wheel chair, and took me for a wheeled walk into the tar-smelling, dusty, summer-strange, outside world.

The air was warm, tasted of memories. The pebble-brown road outside the hospital slithered round a bend and disappeared. A boy on a bicycle rode slowly past, his hands on top of the handle bars. A car crackled past. I was stranded, unable to follow.

134

We crossed the road and entered a deep, green avenue of trees.

"This is the Glen, Peter. This is where the nurses come to do their courting."

"Nurses courting?" I said. "You surprise me."

"Why?"

"They have thermometers where their hearts should be."

"Nonsense. What about this nurse you're courting?"

A bird whistled from a high bundle of branches.

"I'll say this for King Edward's, it has an efficient grapevine."

"Don't dodge the question."

"Ah, well, there's an exception to every rule."

"Do you—er—intend to get married?"

I asked, "Why? Wouldn't that be wise?"

"If it comes off it would be the best thing that could happen. But it would take an exceptional girl."

"I know," I said. "Perhaps I've found her."

"I hope so, Peter, I hope so."

My chair wheeled over the grass of the Glen. In other hospitals other Claires were nursing their patients, other Erics were staring at the corner of their ceiling, other children were twitching toward the dream of normality. Some would get there, some wouldn't. That wasn't important, the journey was.

The sun climbed over the morning, the air was soft and clean. Green and black and brown colored the

135

world, blue and white hung above it. I tasted the summer on my tongue, rolled it round my gums, and swallowed it.

"Shall we go back? It's dinnertime."

"Yes," I said, and we wheeled back through the ordinary morning, back to the low, red hospital.

17

Eric

Eric and I lived together for six months. Ate, slept, talked and laughed in that small room with the flower-curtained windows.

I knew him well but not entirely. Does any one person ever know another entirely? Eric hugged something to himself, some part of his tragic, cheerful life that was his own, shared with no one. His last privacy. At the end of six months, when he went home with the knowledge that he was bed-ridden till his death, a gap, a hole, was created in my life that has never quite been filled.

He had spondylitis, which is euphemistic for medical horror, incurable. The joints, his knees, ankles, vertebrae, were locked. His legs were unbendable, as was his spine. He couldn't turn his head either way. In time his shoulders, then his elbows, his wrists, his fingers, would lock.

"It's the gristle between the bones," he explained to me. "It melts and the bones fuse together. It's a bugger, isn't it?"

Spondylitis is also very painful.

Perhaps that was Eric's last privacy, his sad, happy triumph over the disease that was killing him. I don't know. I can only repeat words, snatches of our six months' conversations, and say, "This is the man, but it isn't the whole man."

Eric recited:

There's a green-eyed, yellow idol
To the north of Katmandu;
There's a little marble cross below the town
Where a broken-hearted woman tends the grave
    of Mad Carew——

"Shut up, Eric," I said.
"Why? Don't you like poetry?"
"Yes, that's why I want you to shut up."
"Ha ha. Very funny. What time is it?"
"God knows."
"You can see the clock from there."
"I can't."
"Why not?"
"My eyes are closed."
He said, "Have you thought about that much?"
"What? Opening my eyes?"

138

"No. God. Religion and all that."

"Yes," I said. "Have you?"

"I've had spondylitis for thirteen years, been in bed for the last five. That answer your question?"

"More or less. What's the result of your thinking?"

"Oh, I think there's something in it. All this, life, couldn't be just an accident. There's a design to it, and if there's a design there must be a designer."

"I don't agree. Life was an accident. As soon as Man as a whole accepts that, he'll accept responsibility for it."

"Are you turning atheist?" said Eric.

"Dunno. Besides, I don't like labels. Even the simplest person, like you, for instance, is much too complex for one label. Before I got polio I was a lukewarm Methodist with a faintly puzzled mind."

"And what are you now?"

"A passionate believer in the theory that Man in a later stage of his evolution won't need spiritual crutches. He'll have the knowledge to do without 'em."

"But that's in the future," said Eric. "What about now?"

"Well, if I accept that theory—and I do—I can't accept God now, can I? If that's being an atheist, then I'm an atheist."

"That's all very well, very intelligent and all that, but won't you need something to help you face up to life?"

"Yes," I said. "But what I'll need is inside myself. In other words, I need myself to face up to myself. And if I can't find it inside myself I won't find it anywhere. Religion is an excuse, and I haven't got any excuses."

"Not for me it isn't," said Eric. "It's what I need."

"And if a thing is needed it's necessary."

"Exactly. You know, this religious thing is very personal. What suits one man might not suit another, but that isn't to say one man is dead right and the other dead wrong. It's probably the most personal thing in life. More personal than the nurses giving you a bottle."

"That wouldn't be so bad if they didn't have cold hands. I'm glad to see we agree on something."

He said, "If Life is an accident, how did the accident happen?"

"Well, the amino acids and what-not got together in the sludge of prehistory and said, 'Let's get together and create something, we've nothing better to do.' So they did and the first Thing crawled out of the swamp. Must have looked a bit like you."

"Thanks. Where's evolution going to take us?"

"I've already told you. To a fulfillment of ourselves as self-sufficient entities."

"Seems a bit soulless. No color or emotion. More like human patterns than human beings."

"There would be color. And emotion. Those things are human, not God-given. What would be lacking is the narrow dogma or religion, the rigid adherence to a way of life in the eroding belief that it is the correct one, the only one. The pomp and superstition of the Church would no longer be necessary. Man would realize he is Man. That the responsibility is his."

"There's just one thing," said Eric. "When people know your beliefs, your atheism, they're going to put it down to your being crippled. A rejection of God because of what happened to you."

"Atheism is a form of religion, much wider and more satisfying than Christianity. People are free to think what they will, I don't want to change the world, just find myself."

"How do you mean?"

"As long as I can apply the test of absolute honesty, as long as I know that my beliefs are the results of objective thought and not a form of physical revenge, then it doesn't matter what other people think. If I can see the truth as it applies to myself I'll be safe."

"Now you're talking about the basic thing in life. The truth. Honesty. If more people got rid of their personal prejudices, took their ostrich heads from the sands of their own importance, and took a good long look at themselves and the world—as you have to do when you find yourself crippled, for instance—they'd be better for it."

"If they didn't die of shock."

141

He said, "Stick to the truth, Pete, whatever you do. Don't betray it, don't even compromise with it, or you'll end up disliking yourself."

Because he believed in the truth, Eric asked the doctors about himself. Arrangements were made for him to go home to his wife and family.

"There's no point in staying here, there's nothing more they can do," he said. "Apart from which, they've given me the hint that I'm occupying a bed that could be put to better use."

It wasn't a bitter remark, just an honest one. I was to be given the same hint, a standard practice with incurables.

One morning I left the ward and Eric. I hung in my slings and tried to move what wouldn't move, tried to fight what had to be fought a different way. At dinnertime I went back. The ambulance had called, and Eric had gone. A nurse was dusting the top of the cleared-out locker that had been his.

"Eric asked me to say 'Good-by' for him," she said and went on dusting.

I knew him, part of him, and through him I came to know myself.

18

Home

The summer months of 1958 were heavy, stuffed with concrete days and leaden weeks. I could feed and shave myself, one-handed. I could sit in a vertical position for some two hours, though I still couldn't move my chair. My left arm strengthened but wouldn't straighten. My breathing was adequate. The hospital had given its usual hint on occupying beds that could be put to better use. Now was the time to go home, stretch my second life to see how it fared in the normal world.

❀   ❀   ❀

October. I hung in my slings and watched the autumn through the window. Black trees and leaves drifting down like solemn tears. A low, gray, windy sky. Cold air and stamping feet, scarves and gloves and overcoats and

143

lights on early. Christmas. Christmas was outside, invisible and distant, waiting.

Another hospital Christmas. One couldn't be avoided, but not two. Surely not two? Christmas in a hospital is very cautious; it tiptoes down the hygienic corridors and washes its hands before it greets you; it doesn't speak loudly, and it's locked away at ten-thirty every night. Even the beer tasted of antibiotics. No, not another hospital Christmas.

My left arm flexed with half-life. The rest was dead. For how long? Forever, it seemed. Living with that would need a new sort of courage, not the once-in-a-while mighty effort, but a daily living which no one would notice. If they did notice I would have failed. Failed who? The great, fat mass of people I didn't know? My family? Claire? Myself? All of them, but myself most of all.

Could a cripple live in ordinary family life? The day-to-day attention, the dependence on others who might be tired or busy. Would the cripple feel he was in the way, a burden, and if he did would it destroy him?

And could this cripple marry? Earn a living? Raise a family? Or were they untouchable ideals?

Only one thing was certain: I would never know if I had to stay in a hospital. Or live in a Home—a Home for Incurables. What a deadly, rusty, sadistic thought! I had to get home, expand my narrow, new life into the fullness of normality. I had to!

A hand touched my shoulder. "Peter."

"Oh. Sorry, I was thinking."

"You were miles away."

It was the ward Sister, who was a man. A small, fair, eager, fussy man who always said "The point is" before he said anything else.

"How would you like to go home?" he asked. Just like that.

"Home?"

"The point is, we think it would be best for you to be at home. How long would it take to get things arranged? Get a bed downstairs and so on?"

"About a fortnight." I said the first thing that came into my head. I was afraid he would vanish in a puff of smoke.

"A fortnight. Good, good. The point is, you'll be better at home, won't you?" He fussed away, beaming his good deed at everybody.

The leaves drifting from the black trees were like confetti, not tears. The sky was less sullen. No tiptoeing hospital Christmas. My Christmas was outside, my Christmas was in my own home. Home. In a fortnight, a mere fortnight.

❊   ❊   ❊

"I'm going home," I said to the nurse who dressed me.

"In a fortnight," I said to the cleaning women who mopped the floors.

145

"Home, in a fortnight," I said to the physiotherapist. I wrote to Claire: *I'm going home in a fortnight.*

It's the most wonderful news I've ever heard, she wrote. *Now we'll be able to see each other at least once a week on my day off. I'll come to Rotherham, and we'll go in the park, or go shopping, or just sit in front of the fire and talk. I'm so happy.*

"I'm coming home," I said to my father and my sister.

"Home?" they asked together. "What's this about home?"

"The Sister says so."

" 'Sfunny they've said nothing to us," said my father. "Is the doctor around? I'll ask him about it."

He went in search of the doctor.

"In a fortnight," I beamed at my sister.

The doctor strode up the ward, my father following him. I beamed at them.

"What's this about home?" asked the doctor.

"The Sister said I could. In a fortnight."

The doctor glanced at my father. The beginnings of an icicle touched my heart. Then I knew what he was going to say, knew as surely as if I'd already heard him, and my freezing heart pleaded, "Don't say it! For Christ's sake, don't say it!" But he did. His mouth opened, his lips moved with tremendous slowness, crawled round the words which dropped like petrified pebbles into the well of my shattered hope, "I don't know where you—or the Sister—got that idea from.

146

It will be a long time before you're able to go home."

Two tears oozed over the rims of my eyes, dribbled like clear blood down my cheeks. I couldn't stop them, I didn't even try.

19

Forward and Backward

The ward Sister, that small, fair, fussy man, spoke to me only when he had to, and he avoided my eyes. He crept in and crept out as if he thought the ceiling would fall if he made a sudden, unplanned movement. But I wasn't angry, not even when they failed to explain how the mistake was made. A misunderstood sentence, perhaps, or a crackling telephone wire; his own eagerness, his own desire, to claim credit, had done the rest. He was a man who liked claiming credit: when the sun shone he would put on his aren't-I-clever face, and when it rained he would be faintly apologetic.

I wasn't angry, I wasn't anything. I exercised, I ate, I slept, I wrote letters, I existed. A hard, brittle shell grew around me through which nothing could reach, not even Claire. And inside the shell was the soft fear of the future, which stretched blank and black into an infinity of years. I was stripped of clay wonders, empty prayers; the future was a brain and half an arm. A blank, black fear in a hard, white shell.

Could colors be painted on the blackness, windows put in the blankness? Home? Claire? Marriage? Kids? Writing?

Were these the paint and the glass?

Out of myself would come the strength. I was alone. From the depths of myself would come the paint to color the blackness of the future and the putty to fix the windows in its blankness. Only I could start the climb, I on my dead legs climbing, reaching, scrambling into the future, filling the nothingness with the trinkets of living; only I could paint the future and fix the windows in it; only I could make myself live. I was the Shaper, the Maker, the Carver of my second life. And I would live because there was no alternative, except death. It was how I would live, how I would shape and make and carve and color the future that was my own private, personal possession.

The hard, white, brittle shell began to splinter.

❀   ❀   ❀

The trousers had creases in them like stair rods, and the shirt irritated my shoulders. A nurse was at the other end, lacing my shoes.

"How long is it since you last wore shoes?" she said.

"Eleven months and three days."

"Think what you've saved in shoe-repair bills," she said. "I always seem to be at the cobbler's."

"It's eleven months and three days since I wore anything. Apart from these delightful Dior hospital gowns in delicate blue-and-white sackcloth with overtones of gravy stains."

She sniffed. Hospitals were her temples, Flo Nightingale her God, and jokes about either were heresy.

"What time do you leave?" she said.

"Ten. Back at seven. Nine hours of blessed release."

"You're very fortunate. All our patients aren't allowed to spend a Sunday at home."

"P'raps as well, sweetheart. What would you do all day if everybody went home?"

She ignored the question. "Is Claire going with you?" The tone of her voice left the unspoken by-law, "Nurses should not form romantic attachments with their patients," hovering uneasily in the antiseptic air.

I said, "She'll be arriving about twelve. We're getting married this afternoon, get the double bed ready."

"That's not very funny."

She drew back the curtains, and I saw the beginning blue of the clouded sky. This was the day, the anxious, eager day. The testing day.

The nurse sniffed. "Sun's trying to shine," she said. "That'll be nice for you."

❋   ❋   ❋

150

It might never have happened. It might have been an eleven-month nightmare, with this the waking morning. Waking to a drive in the country in a neighbor's car with Ted, and Allan, my brother-in-law, and Kevin, my three-year-old nephew, wide-eyed and silent with the strangeness of the morning.

It might never have happened except for the strap holding me to the seat. It might never have happened except for the collapsed wheel chair crammed in the boot of the car.

But the sun was shining, and the conversation was as crisp as the unreal morning, "What's it feel like, being out?"

"Like being released from prison," I said.

"Dot's been going mad this morning. Dusted the furniture at least four times."

"If you find a speck of dust keep quiet about it."

Nearer, nearer. The black edge of Sheffield; the gray, gasping chimneys of the solemn steel works; the avenues of grim walls.

I said, "Brass band standing by?"

"And the Mayor."

"Taken us three days and nights to get all the flags up."

"When's this nurse of yours coming?"

"Dinnertime."

"Good," said Allan. "I'll take her out this afternoon."

"You're married," said Ted. "I'll take her."

151

"You're both wrong," I said. "I'm taking her. Or she's taking me."

"Where to?"

"The park, probably. We'll go and see if it's changed much."

"Go and do a bit of snogging, you mean. Crafty devil."

Rotherham disfigured the land. We crept between the sad factories, along Main Street, passed the Sunday-shuttered shops.

"You'll see changes in this place," said Allan. "One or two new shops gone up. They say they're going to build a bus station."

"They've been saying that for years."

Clifton Park, vast and green, a carnival of whispering nights and shouting days, the yard of my childhood, slipped away behind us.

Middle Lane. Cambridge Street. The last corner, the letter box needs painting, needed painting before I went away.

North Crescent.

The same houses, the same glowing redness of the slow street curve under a different sun.

The car stopped. The red wheel chair was set up on the pavement. The curious Crescent curtains slyly stirred. Dot sauntered casually down the garden path, and Kevin watched, wide-eyed with questions, as I was lifted from the car into the waiting wheel chair.

The dream of the morning was still intact.

Claire arrived at twelve. She walked into the room and smiled her unique smile.

"Hello," she said. "This is the first time I've seen you dressed."

❁   ❁   ❁

The sun sunk like a moon over the cardboard, afternoon park.

"I love you," said Claire. She was sitting on the grass, her arm across my knees, her head on her arm. My weak fingers touched the fairness of her hair.

"And I you."

"Soon I'll be able to come every week. When you're home for good."

"Roll on that happy day."

"Do you mind very much?"

"Mind what?"

"Being in hospital."

"I'm not getting any further forward. I want to get out, earn a living. Get married."

She said, "Is that a proposal?"

"Yes."

Her dress, spread on the grass, circled her like a promise. Her fingers reached for mine. The cardboard park heard our secrets and kept them.

She said, "We'll have a bungalow."

"We'll buy it with buttons."

"You can write, Peter. I know you can."

"Might take a long time before we can afford to get married."

"We've a lifetime. Two lifetimes, mine and yours."

"Where shall we build this bungalow?" I asked.

"Anywhere. So long as we can be together. It'll have three bedrooms."

"And a study for me to work in."

"And a nursery."

"How many kids?"

"Three. Two girls and a boy."

"And a large garden where they can play."

"And a tiled bathroom with a sunken bath."

"Very exotic."

"And a green roof. It must have a green roof."

"What about servants' quarters?"

"We don't want servants. Just you and me, together."

"And the three kids."

"And the three kids."

"It sounds perfect."

"It will be perfect, Peter, it will be."

The sun, like a moon, slipped down the sky, but we didn't notice. Outside the world, outside time, we fashioned paper castles in the paper air and suffered the ache of utter happiness.

❋   ❋   ❋

The car crawled toward the hospital. Nothing much was said. Sheffield sorrowed our passing. The headlights chipped at the darkness like cold chisels.

"Nearly there," said Allan.

"Wonder if they'll let me come next week."

"Should imagine so. Ask 'em if you can come for the weekend."

"And I'll ask 'em if I can come for Christmas."

"Nearly there," said Ted.

The last corner; the dip in the road; the final slowing of the car.

"Here we are. Five minutes to seven—we're early."

The lights of the hospital gleamed like cold jewels on the fingers of a giant, black hand.

❀   ❀   ❀

November. Home for every weekend. Friday evening to Sunday teatime. Two living days in each dead week. Questions. Answers. Confusion.

"We've been to the Housing Department. They say we'll have to move."

"Why?"

"To a house with a front room. So's you can have a room to yourself."

"What about Dot?" My sister and her family lived in a house on the other side of the Crescent.

"That's the difficulty. The hospital says you can't go home unless there's somebody on hand during the day.

155

With your mother dead, and Dad and Ted at work, that would have to be Dot."

"What does the Housing Department say?"

"They'll put us on the list but we can't be given any priority."

"But that'll take years and years!"

"I know."

The smell, the taste, the fog of winter never reached the ward. It was baffled by the antiseptic windows. I shuttled backward and forward between the hospital and home, the week and the weekend, the conscious and the unconscious.

It was arranged that I spend Christmas week at home.

December. Twenty-five steps to Christmas and six down the other side into the New Year. Garbled carols at a cold door:

Goo' King Wenslass looked out,
Pain was cruel, gatherin' win'er fuel.
Hole in my stocking, hole in my shoe, God bless
    you.

"Thanks, mister, Merry Christmas. How much? Two-pence! Stingy owd bugger. Try next door."

Cards dropped through the letter box like king-sized snowflakes.

"One here from Aunt Ethel. Haven't sent her one."

Lights. Orange street lights burning the fog. Cotton-wool shop windows. More carols, more cards.

"Haven't had one from our George. We sent him one."

Claire stayed with us for four days, four glowing days.

In a million homes a million fireside philosophers philosophized, "Ah, well. Another year. Nineteen fifty-nine. Wonder what this one'll bring? A decent summer, I hope. Cheers."

"We haven't arranged our holidays yet. I hope we haven't left it too late."

"I see the Russians are being difficult again. We aren't firm enough with 'em, that's half the trouble. We aren't even firm enough with the Yanks."

"Montgomery ought to be in politics."

"I hope our Victor doesn't marry that girl. Her father drinks."

"So does Victor's father."

"That's not the same. Cheers."

"I can see United getting promotion this year. Good manager. Personal friend of mine."

"For God's sake don't get drunk again. I nearly died on Christmas Eve when you crawled in on your hands and knees."

"Besides, she's been seeing this other boy behind Victor's back. It isn't gossip."

"He once asked my advice about team selection—oh, well, if you don't want to listen."

"Majorca this year, I think . . ."

"Monty wouldn't stand for it . . ."

"We weren't firm enough over Suez . . ."

"Played Newcastle in the Cup . . ."

"There are nicer girls than her . . ."

"Sick all over their new carpet . . ."

"I think I've had too much . . ."

"I've just seen two of my wife . . ."

"Christ! What a shock . . ."

"Listen, you. That's my wife you're . . ."

"That's your bad . . ."

"Quiet! Quiet, everybody. The clock's striking."

"It's twelve."

"Join hands, everybody!"

"Should auld acquaintance be forgot!"

"Happy New Year!"

"Happy New Year."

"Happy New Year. . . ."

A car stopped in front of a hospital. A red wheel chair was taken from the boot and unfolded. Two men lifted a third from the car into the wheel chair, then pushed it into the silent building.

❉   ❉   ❉

Nineteen hundred and fifty-nine. January thawed into February. I wrote to Claire:

What it amounts to is this: the hospital says I can't go home to a house with one downstairs room. The housing people will put us at the end of the list which will take years. Then there's still the problem of being looked after during the day. Confusing, isn't it?

March. My twentieth birthday. Sixteen months away from my admittance into the hospital. I received fewer cards than I received on my nineteenth birthday.

"We've seen the Council. About you going home."

"What did they say?"

"Well, when you do go they'll alter the lavatory, make it bigger so's you can get in and out on a toilet chair."

"That's nice."

"It's something, anyway."

March blew into a weepy April.

"We're willing to give it a try," said the family. "If we wait for the Housing Department and the hospital to arrive at a solution you'll be here forever more."

I asked to see the doctor, and they wheeled me into a small, private room. The doctor bustled busily in.

"What's this about, Peter?" he asked.

"I'd like to go home."

"You go home for the weekends."

"I mean for good."

"Oh," he said. "I see. Well, I can't make you stay here against your will. But it's against my advice."

"I don't intend stopping here for several years, Doctor. I've a life to live."

"If you must go, you must. There's nothing more to be said."

He swirled through the door, his starched gown clattering emptily against the wood.

❋   ❋   ❋

On the first of May, a Friday evening, a car stopped outside the hospital, as it had done every Friday evening for seven months. A youth was lifted from a wheel chair into the car, as he had been at the beginning of every weekend for a long time. The chair was folded and put in the boot as usual. Then a suitcase was put in the boot on top of the chair, and that had never happened before. The car started, stalled, jolted through the hospital gates into the mild, spring evening.

20

The Small Things

The Crescent hadn't changed: red-faced houses with lacy eyes and mouths like brown doors; a rope of pebbles between verges like old, green carpets, thrown away; prim hedges martyred with the wounds of gateways; shopping-bag people crawling to the invisible shops; floods of children at the four o'clock breaching of the school dam; guilty chimneys secretly smoking; aproned harems of gossip in the sun-shadows.

"She never is!"

"She is. Sure as I'm standing here."

"But it's only five months since she got married. I watched 'em come out of church. White didn't suit her."

"She never said anything to me."

"It's not the sort of thing you like to talk about, is it?"

"I think it's shocking! Five months! I had to wait ten years before the Council gave me a house."

The Crescent was unchanged; my eighteen hospital months hadn't touched it. Two winters and an autumn hadn't frozen it; two springs and a summer hadn't warmed it; a year and a half of the tragic trivialities of its captive families hadn't scarred it.

I was changed: now my world was on wheels, and the small things, like the raised edge of a paving stone, were dangerous.

      ❋   ❋   ❋

"Oops," said Claire. "It's the front wheels at the front, they aren't big enough."

"It's the paving stones," I said. "That one's stuck up about two inches."

"Good job you're strapped in."

The sweat trickled down my spine, dampened my castrating corset. The June sun irritated me. I wanted to strip and dive into a world of water, away from the sticky heat of summer. A tired bus ambled past and kicked a spiteful cloud of dust at us. Behind me, Claire coughed and gasped:

"That went in my eye!"

The red wheel chair stopped. She fumbled for her handkerchief while I waited. And I thought, "In other circumstances I would leap to her aid, gently clear her gritty eye with the tender corner of my masculine handkerchief, receive her grateful smile with modesty, and

162

stroll with her into the park. In other circumstances."

A small thing. The wheel chair started again. A youth walked past, his arm round the summer waist of a dark-haired girl. They tried not to look at me. Another small thing.

"Let's sit down," said Claire. "I'm boiled."

She sat on a wooden bench under a wide tree and said, "You're quiet today."

"Am I? Must be the sun."

"Thought you liked the summer."

"I do. Or I think I do. I did once."

"How's the writing going?"

"Haven't done any."

"Why?"

"Couldn't. Let's get engaged."

"Don't change the subject."

"I'm not. Let's get engaged."

"Not yet." She stabbed the path with her toe.

"Why?"

"It's too soon. We have to get organized."

"Get some money, you mean."

"We have to see how things are going to be."

"What's that supposed to mean?"

"Let's not quarrel."

But the burning park stuck small needles of memory into me.

"Why not?" I said.

"We quarreled last week when I came."

"Ah, yes. About why had you to go home early. I remember. Wonder if we'll quarrel next week?"

"I hope not."

"Why? May as well do the hat trick."

"Let's go back." She pushed me through the park gates, through the burning afternoon, fueled with small things. Perhaps the need to belong, to feel useful, was only a small thing.

"Thursday's my day off next week," said Claire. "I may be a bit later than usual."

❋   ❋   ❋

The future was mine to shape and mold. But with what tools? Writing? A knack of nailing words together? The stories I had written lay like dead ducklings on their pages. No color, no reality, no life, no anything. A brain and an arm. Were these the shapers of the future, the carvers of the years? And if they were, were they sharp enough?

Could I do it? God couldn't help, He was the invention of Man. A belief in this invention would dull my tools, cloud my brain, make my hand unsteady with the weight of platitudes. But with the platitudes and the narrow dogma burned away, a new strength might come, a strength not of faith for the sake of faith, but of fact and reality. And the success, not of money or small fame, but the secret success of fulfillment which is the only success worth working for.

And illusion wouldn't shatter because there would be no illusion.

21

This is the Window

This is the window I watched through. There is the hedge; her head was only just visible above that hedge, and it isn't very high. About five feet. And there is the street she walked on—quick, eager footsteps, nearly running and always happy. And the bus stop is invisible from here, but it's there just the same. Oh, the delight of reaching a welcome bus stop!

This is the hand that touched her—these weak, ordinary fingers made strong with the contact of her softness, her warmth. And these ears heard her voice and the eagerness; these useless handles on the side of my head knew the gold of her words. These eyes have marvelled at the depth in hers. This mouth has whispered, "Claire."

No more. These ears heard her words, "I think it best

if I don't come again." And these eyes saw the unbreakable truth on her face.

I've put her letters in a suitcase, hidden her photograph. Now I need a suitcase for the memories and a hiding place for the dream.

Like torn paper our plans, our bungalow, our "We'll-laugh-at-the-world" hope, drift down, pile themselves like dead confetti round my still feet.

There are no words to speak, no reasons to give. "We quarreled too much." "The future isn't very certain." "Best to make a clean break now." These are excuses, not reasons.

No pain lasts forever. Even the memories will fade like old photographs. But if success came would it be as sweet? Is success for one as good as success for two? Or is it mockery if it isn't shared?

"I think it best if I don't come again."

These ears heard and knew. These eyes saw and believed. There is an end to every dream. It's best to face it, stiff upper lip and all that, other women in the world.

"I think it best . . ."

Only a hospital romance, they're never very serious. Forget, forget, forget.

". . . if I don't come again."

There is the street, there is the hedge—her head was only just visible above that—and this is the window.

167

22

Humangosophy

A hollow room in a hollow world; a dusky, winter, house-vanishing, hollow world seen through the window of the hollow room. The dusk invaded the window, sneaked in when it blinked, dirtied the ceiling, smudged the walls, until only the pilot light of the radiogram was visible and the only sound was the marching music of Ravel, laying siege to the dirty ceiling and smudged walls.

Dusk; the happy touch of darkness; the blotting out of the visible; the time for thought, for contented reflection, for the warmth of music. Is there a better time of day than dusk?

Someone knocked on the door.

"Come in!"

The Welfare Man and his assistant broke into my hollow cave of dusky music.

"I'll put the light on," said the Welfare Man. He pressed the switch, murdering my deep shadows with flat light.

"That's better," he said, pleased with himself.

He was a tall man who wore his own importance like a striped overcoat. He had the air of a St. Bernard with a full cask of rum beneath its charitable chin. It was his task to dispense this rum, even to people who thought they weren't thirsty. His assistant was a fair and friendly woman who lived on the same level as other people.

I faded the rampaging Ravel into a whispering world of his own.

"I've come about the—er—extensions to your toilet," he said. "I have the plans here."

"Well done. It's only taken a year."

"Now, now, Peter. There's committees to see, people who have to approve these things. Have a look at the plan."

He spread a sheet of paper across my knees, then stood back, holding hands with himself.

"The figures down the side are the measurements," he said. "Height, length, overall floor area and so on. Is it suitable?"

The plan was a collection of lines which meant nothing to me. "Looks big enough," I nodded, wisely.

The fair and friendly assistant said: "How about coming to our place on Monday?"

"What place is that?"

"The Welfare Department. Occupational therapy, rug pegging, stool making."

"We'll provide the toilet chair, of course," said the Welfare Man. "I'm here now to find out if you think it'll be suitable."

"Yes," I said. "I'm not a very good rug pegger. Or stool maker."

"How do you know?" she said.

"So you think they're suitable?" said the Welfare Man.

"Yes, I think they're suitable," I said. "The idea doesn't appeal to me. It's passing time for the sake of passing time. Not a very rewarding process."

"I can see your point," she said, "but won't you give it a try? Shall we send our taxi for you next Monday?"

"All right, I'll give it a try. I could be wrong."

"You're quite certain," said the Welfare Man, "about these plans?"

"I've said so four times," I snarled. "Would you like it in writing?"

"Now, now, now, now," he spluttered, "now, now, now. We have to be sure. This is going to cost a lot of money. Over a hundred pounds."

I opened my mouth, but the assistant spoke first, "The taxi will call around two, then. We'll see you on Monday."

On his way out the Welfare Man forgave me by saying, "I'll leave the light on for you. It must be depressing sitting in the dark."

❀   ❀   ❀

The bare-board vault of a room was like a forgotten church. Two long tables squatted in the center of this room. These were the altars, the wheel chaired, crutched, walking-sticked worshipers crouched over them, threading raffia into the seats of stools that would never be sat on or pegging rugs with the unremembered remnants of another time.

I was one of the worshipers at this Monday shrine of uselessness. I squeezed paint from a tube onto the outline of a flower on a tray cloth. I made a red circle which was like the afternoon, it had no beginning and no end.

Whispered words wandered through the cathedral of the day.

"She says she never gets a Christmas card. Not one."

"That's misery for you."

"I thought my life was bad enough. It's worse when you can't get around under your own steam."

And faces peered through the legs of stools at the wheel chairs.

"Under your own steam, that's everything."

I oozed a green petal onto the edge of my red circle.

"Coming to the film next week?"

171

"Yes. Hope it's better than the last one."

"Bit weird, wasn't it."

"Yes. You'd think they could get something better than that."

My red circle grew three green petals. I thought, "Why come? Why are you here, you whispering voices, trapped in your useless stools, smothering under your pegged, forgotten rugs? There's a world out there, outside this dead church of a room. Join it, for pity's sake! You're alive, aren't you? You're alive."

But the dead voices whispered round the dead room. Dead voices in living mouths, roaring their dead whispers over my bowed, painting head.

"She doesn't get on with her husband. Expects too much of him. It isn't as if she can't do more, she can, but she won't try."

"It's ninety-nine per cent will power. Where's my crutches?"

"He is cheerful, that lad. I don't know how he does it, him being like he is."

Old young faces, grim eyes of suffering, legs of stools like prison bars, suffocating rugs. "You're alive, damn you! I shouldn't be here. All we have in common is our crippledness. That's all!"

The Welfare Man came from his office. He walked round the tables dripping goodness over his charges. He stopped behind my chair.

"My, that's good, Peter," he beamed. "That's good. Tea and buns coming soon, everybody."

My red circle was surrounded by green petals, each one touching the next. My flower was trapped in the prison of itself. Would the afternoon ever end?

        ❀   ❀   ❀

I was a pupil at this school, this gray-bricked childhood of many people. This long drive knew my feet; frightened, reluctant, dragging feet, anonymous in a nine o'clock feet forest.

And now my nephew's feet took him to the same school.

"Just in time," said Dot. "They'll be out any minute."

Three-thirty. The green doors crashed outward, and children swarmed down the steps like bees.

"Hiya, Mum. Hiya, Pete."

Kevin climbed onto the footplate of the chair. We were followed by a crowd of silent, wide-eyed children; the wise, innocent eyes of children not yet marked with the savage scars of growing up. They missed nothing, but there was no adult knowledge there, only a warm bath of curiosity. And the eyes began to find voices.

"You been poorly, mister?"

"Yes."

"In a hospital?"

"Yes."

"My gramma's been in 'ospital. She 'ad a noperation."

"What for?"

"Dunno. They wouldn't tell me."

"Bet she didn't come out in a wheel chair. All of 'em don't, do they, mister?"

"No, not all of them."

"Wish I 'ad a wheel chair."

"An' me."

"I'd race you."

"It's got brakes on—look!"

"Them's not brakes!"

"Are them brakes, mister?"

"Yes, they're br——"

"Tell'd yer, big 'ead!"

At the end of the drive, "So long, mister. See yer tomorrer."

"So long."

An adult man and woman walked past and tried not to look at me because they knew better than children, they knew that you shouldn't stare at a cripple.

Why can't we die before the age of puberty? Afterward it's too late.

       ✻   ✻   ✻

"There is something! I know it!" I shouted at the quicksands.

And the quicksands bubbled, "Forget it. Sink in us, we'll protect you. Forget the normal world."

I shouted, "But I have to be regarded as normal. Can't you see that?"

"But you aren't normal, are you? A wheel chair, half an arm—that isn't normal."

"It's only relative," I said. "If most people were in wheel chairs a walking man would be abnormal."

"It's easier our way."

"I want to earn a living."

"The State gives you a pension. Don't be ungrateful."

"I don't want their bloody pension!"

"There's people to take you out——"

"I want to earn my——"

"To the seaside, even. Film show once a month——"

"I have to be bigger than my chair."

"No worries in us. No need for any effort. Charity's yours for the taking."

"Damn your charity! Damn your film show! And your organized-because-it's-our-civic-duty-to-organize trips to the seaside! I need the worry, the pain, the frustration, the weather of the world. Are you blind?"

"You're mad," sneered the quicksands. "And ungrateful. And awkward."

"Because I won't conform to your pattern? Because I won't accept that a cripple is different from anybody else, a robot needing rigid lines of treatment, same for all cripples just because they're crippled? You can't herd people like cows."

175

"Try us. It won't be much different, you'll still have your working hand——"

"To pull the shroud over my face?"

"No, no, no, no. Don't be silly. 'Tisn't a bad life in us, even though you are—as you are. Make the most of what you've got."

"No," I said, "I'm going to make the most of what I haven't got. I'm going to take this worrying world by the ordinary scruff of its normal neck and shout, 'Remember me? I've come back. I don't need your sick pity and sicker charity! I need your acceptance, your indifference, even! Forget the wheel chair, it isn't important.'"

But the quicksands hissed and bubbled, never very far away.

Seventeen months after the idea was first suggested, the extension to our lavatory was finished. A toilet chair was provided. After two and a half years, bed-pan years, I sat in this kingdom of privacy, prouder than a king on a new throne.

But there was a snag: ever afterward, whenever he visited the house, the Welfare Man wanted to know whether "the extension was suitable" and "was it being used regularly?" And we had to stroke him with our gratitude, the way one strokes a nervous cat, otherwise I don't think he would have been happy.

❋   ❋   ❋

I said, "The fact that I asked for you isn't proof that when Man is near death he needs God. Or a God."

"Still, you asked for me," said the Minister.

"In my delirium. I'd no idea that I was dying."

"When did you know?"

"About six months after. I heard the doctors gave me a fifty-fifty chance the night I was admitted."

"You seemed relieved when I came."

"You were an antidote. I was pleased to see anybody who took my mind off the pain."

"Where, in your opinion, is Man going?"

"To an awareness of himself. To an acceptance of his own responsibility. If he doesn't blow himself to bits first."

"Which God will prevent."

I said, "We carry the present with us all the time. It's like walking down a dark corridor, carrying a candle. The dark closes behind us, opens before us. If the light vanishes, Man will have blown it out with his own incapable breath. There's no mystic God involved."

"Very fanciful. You ought to be a writer."

He left, dragging the burden of his collar.

My second life was emptying itself of rusty trinkets. But would the new ones shine and glow and twinkle? Or would it remain empty?

23

Cards

Half past eight. Or is it nine? Can't be nine or the nurse would be here. Too many shadows on the clock's morning face. What day is it? Isn't there something special about today? I remember thinking last night, there's something special about tomorrow. It's tomorrow today. I can't think this time in a morning. There ought to be a law against it. No thinking before noon, transgressors will be made to listen to "Mrs. Dale's Diary" for a week. They'd never do it again.

My bed's comfortable. Two pillows under my head, one under my back, two under my knees. And two cushions supporting my feet. The prescribed thing for the polio. Who'd think five pillows and two cushions could be comfortable? Well, they are. And a pile of blankets on top. A pillows-body-blankets sandwich. Salt, anyone?

Funny what a person can get used to. If I'd known, four years ago, that I would have to sleep stretched flat on my back, I would've said, "Impossible—lose my curled-up warmth, my knees on my chest, my hand between my knees, like a hibernating hedgehog. I'd never get to sleep stretched flat." Now I sleep on my back as though I've been doing it all my life.

There aren't many things I do miss when I think about it. Of course, I miss walking, miss my independence, but I don't envy other people. I've heard some cripples say things like, "I'd give anything to walk like you" or "I wish I was healthy like she is." I wouldn't give anything to be like somebody else. If I can't be Marshall walking, then I'd rather be Marshall crippled than be anybody else. And my first life, I don't miss that very much. Not that I don't think about it. It's like having a box of chocolates that nobody else knows about. Every so often I take out a chocolate memory, unwrap it, taste it, and put it back again. That's the best of these chocolates, I can taste them over and over, they never get sticky or lose their flavor. I know when to put the lid on the box, too. That's important. If I left the lid off I might get neurotic indigestion.

And my second life. There aren't many chocolates in that yet. I want to write, but what? My short stories are rubbish. Perhaps that's important, the fact that I know they're rubbish and yet keep writing them. A book, a novel? An autobiography? That's conceited, everybody writes autobiographies. Some people have only to have a tooth out, and they write a book about it. All the autobiographies I've read by people who've been ill or injured have been too full of false modesty and nobleness in the face of suffering and devoted nurses. Too full of the personal pronoun, as though illness had made them special people. I couldn't write a book like that; I'd vomit all over the typewriter.

But perhaps the limits of autobiography could be pushed back a little, giving the writer more freedom. If I ever write an autobiography it'll be because I need to for my own sake, not to glorify my illness to other people. All these books glorifying conquest over physical suffering are wrong; you don't conquer it, you arrive at an armed truce. And nobility through suffering is tripe. You're not a better person, only a different one.

Twenty to nine. This is one of my favorite times of day, this waiting in the shrinking morning darkness of the empty house. My other favorite time is dusk on an autumn day. It doesn't have to be a picture-book dusk either; smell of burning leaves, migrating birds across a pale sky, crispness in the air, and all that tripe that happens only in films. It can be raining, or blowing a gale, or black with fog, or freezing the you-know-whats off a brass monkey. If it's dusk and it's autumn, then it's different and I like it.

It isn't autumn now, it's March. March—that's it! That's what's special about today!

It's my twenty-first birthday!

And I didn't remember. Wonder how many cards I've got. Wish somebody would come in now. Who hasn't bought me a present? A watch from Dad, a dressing case from Dot and Allan, a signet ring from Ted. That leaves—mustn't let my mercenary streak show. I've got one but I mustn't let it show.

Twenty-one. I've been alive since nineteen thirty-nine. Six months before the war started. Not that my birth started that particular waste of six years. I've seen films of the war, the real war, not the Hollywood one. A German burning in a ditch he'd never seen before. His flames weren't any more noble because they were ours; they burned same as other flames. I don't expect that German was thinking about glorious victory over the British at that moment. And the man who set him alight, he couldn't have felt too good about it. War's a worse disease than polio, but they don't stand with their nagging tins on drafty corners, collecting pennies for it. They rake in taxes, then say, "We're very sorry, you don't want war, we don't want war, they don't want war, but we have to defend something or other." They make heroic films about it when it's over, but there's nothing heroic in war, even the heroes are cowards or they wouldn't be there in the first place. I hope they delay the next war, the nuclear one, until I've written something worth reading. Then they can do what they like. One thing they won't do is make films about it when it's over.

The door opened, and my sister came in. She dumped a thick pile of envelopes on my chest.

"This all?" I said. There were about thirty.

"That's all. Never mind, there's another post at twelve. Happy Birthday."

"Ta. Let's get 'em opened."

We flipped open the envelopes, one by one.

"This's a nice one. Nice verse, too."

"I always forget to read the verse. One here from Claire."

Cards all over the place. A snowstorm of cards. A religious one from that chap who's always trying to convert me. He came in one morning and said, "If you believed in God, you would be cured." What sort of a remark is that? He said it before he even said "Good morning," as though it had been on his mind all night. I wonder why he feels it his sacred duty to convert the world? He's always at it, and all he does is make himself a tremendous bore. Is it because that as long as there is somebody, even just one person, who doesn't agree with him, he can't be really certain about his beliefs? I don't try to convert the world to atheism, the whole question's much too personal for one person to show another the way he ought to go.

The Christian is selfish. He tries to solve the world's problems by sitting on his backside in front of an organ, then telling everybody how they ought to live, and if they don't they're doomed to God knows what. I've seen kids, spastic kids with twitching limbs, polio kids with dead limbs, kids with the minds and hearts of kids and bodies of tragedy. It's tragic only if you're crippled as a child. Afterward it's just unfortunate. If somebody asked me what I would like to have again out of my life, I would say "My childhood." I've seen them. Kids trying to walk. Kids trying to be kids. I've seen them draw into themselves when they realized they were different from other kids, without knowing why. I've seen their eyes and it broke my heart.

I'd say this to the Christian, "In the name of the Christ you cherish so blindly, get out of your smug churches, your complacent chapels, and do something bloody well practical! There are so many children, of so many colors, in so many lands, who need so much that there isn't time to put your backside on a pew to listen to some old fool spouting just to make you feel good inside! There isn't even time to pray!" That's what I'd say to the Christian.

"I don't know where we're going to put 'em all," said Dot.

"We can always paper the walls with 'em."

I took a chocolate memory from the box: six cards. That's what I used to get for my birthdays. Never any problem where to put them, they all went on the window sill where nobody looked at them. Now they're all over the place and when people come in, they say, "Haven't you had a lot of cards, aren't you lucky?" And they go round fingering them, playing at being interested. These are the people who have to come, welfare officers, physiotherapist, nurse, not my friends who come to see me and couldn't give a damn whether I've had two thousand cards or none. That's the trouble with cards now; I still only get about six sent to me, the rest are to my wheel chair.

People need re-educating about people like me. We're not a race apart, but that doesn't stop them making remarks like, "It helps to pass his time" or "It's ninety-nine per cent will power" or "If I were him I'd stick my head in the gas oven." And this sort of person relates everything to my wheel chair. If I'm angry or sad they say to one another, "Well, what can you expect, him being like he is?" But I got angry and sad before I ever got polio. It's about as sensible as saying, "That chap behaves like he does because he's left-handed." People need re-educating, but I wouldn't like the job.

"That's the lot," said Dot. She stood the cards on the window sill, on the television, on the bookcase, until the room was almost hidden under this special, twenty-first, card-covered day.

Dot put the envelopes on the fire because they were no more use. The flames crackled round their whiteness, scorched their virginity, blackened their innocence into nothing, and this black nothing was sucked by the wind up the roaring, endless chimney.

Only the cards were left. Only the cards were important.